Sister Plume's

Sister Plume's
Notes on Nursing

A Collection of Letters
to the Editor of *Nursing Times*

Angela Plume, SRN(Lond.)

MACMILLAN

First published 1988

Published by
MACMILLAN EDUCATION LTD
Houndmills, Basingstoke, Hampshire RG21 2XS
and London
Companies and representatives
throughout the world

Typeset by TecSet Ltd, Wallington, Surrey
Printed in Great Britain by
Richard Clay Ltd, Bungay, Suffolk

British Library Cataloguing in Publication Data
Plume, Angela
Sister Plume's notes on nursing.
1. Great Britain. Medicine. Nursing
I. Title   II. Nursing times
610.73'0941
ISBN 0–333–46656–X

Contents

Foreword   Niall Dickson   vii
Acknowledgements   ix
Biography   x

1 **The Home Front**   1
   Ward Rounds   1
   Admission   3
   Discharge   6
   Borrowing   9
   Tidiness   13
   Visiting   16

2 **Of National Moment**   20
   The Griffiths Report   20
   Shift Changes   24
   Nurse Training   27
   Project 2000   31
   Recruitment Crisis   34

3 **Perennial Preoccupations**   38
   Men in Nursing   38
   Uniform   42
   Religious Services   46
   The History of Nursing
       Part I   49
       Part II   51
   Research   54

4   Colleagues and Charlatans   58
     Medical Staff   58
     Alternative Therapies   61
     Meal-Times   65
     Agency Nurses   69
     Privatisation   72
     Letter to a Sister   74

5   Special Occasions   78
     Political Manifesto   78
     Interview   83
     Memorabilia   91

Index   99

Foreword

In these modern days of mediocrity it is rare to come across an individual who combines personal courage with deep insight. It has been my great privilege to know and work with Angela Plume for a number of years and my admiration for her abilities and foresight has continued to grow throughout our acquaintance to the point where it now knows no bounds.

We live in an era where so many of those who are in positions of influence no longer say what they mean or mean what they say. Sister Plume stands out like a beacon of light from these spineless conformists showing the way forward for a perplexed profession. As you will rapidly discover, she is not one to mince her words and her clear moral stance has been an inspiration and example for generations of young nurses.

In this unique collection of letters you will find a reaffirmation of traditional values and a sound critique of those who now claim to lead the profession. Today, with the infernal pressure to change for change's sake, Angela Plume's steadfast defence of all that is sound in nursing will guide us all and help us to choose the righteous path.

This book will, I am sure, become a seminal work used by practitioners throughout the land, and it will serve as a reminder that so long as there are nurses like Angela Plume the welfare of patients will never be at stake.

I commend it to you.

Nursing Times, London WC2, 1988   Niall Dickson

Acknowledgements

This volume is the triumphant culmination of many years' intensive toil — at the bedside by day, and the *escritoire* by night. Those who are not themselves writers can scarcely conceive the sacrifices that are inevitably entailed in a work of this scale. But if others achieve enlightenment through my labours, then I am content.

Some acknowledgements are due to the friends and acquaintances who have made various contributions — albeit modest — to the progress of the work. I know they seek no greater reward than the reflected glory in which they now bask.

The author and publishers wish to acknowledge the following photograph sources:

BBC Hulton Picture Library; Imperial War Museum; Royal College of Nursing.

The publishers have made every effort to trace the copyright holders, but where they have failed to do so they will be pleased to make the necessary arrangements at the first opportunity.

Biography

Angela Plume SRN (Lond.) was born in Morayshire to impover-
ished yet noble parents, in the first half of this century.

Her father, Mr William Plume, had moved north from the
Kentish home of his ancestors to take up a sales position with
the Caledonian Sock Company. He travelled in supportive hose
throughout Scotland, but sadly never made the fortune to
which his talents should surely have entitled him.

The young Angela was — by her own admission — a warm,
caring and attractive child, loved by all those around her. Even
from the age of five, she demonstrated her concern for the
well-being of her fellow man, offering counsel and moral
instruction to all who would listen.

Her mother had very special feelings for her daughter, and it
must have been a blow to them both when the time came for
them to part. Edna Plume was a resolute woman, however, and
having secured a nursing position in London for Angela
— about as far away as it was possible to be — she resigned
herself to a life without Angela. She was to die, a heart-broken
woman, some 40 years later.

Angela settled quickly into her new life, and the rest is
history. Passing her state finals with flying colours at the third
attempt, she began amassing the unique body of clinical
experience which makes her such a valued contributor to all
fields of nursing.

Angela Plume SRN (Lond.) is now a ward sister at St Hilda's,
one of our leading provincial hospitals.

1 The Home Front

Angela Plume first attracted notice with a short yet instructive commentary on the organisation of the traditional ward round, which appeared in the *Nursing Times* on the 13th September 1985.

Nurses of all ages and outlooks warmed to the simplicity and practicality of her advice, and she has since become a national figure.

Today Sister Plume's writings embrace all aspects of nursing — and human — experience. But it is appropriate to begin this anthology with a series of pieces which deal didactically with basic nursing practice and ward management. The following pages provide a comprehensive introduction to the essentials of nursing, and will prove equally fascinating to the student or experienced nurse.

Ward Rounds

Let me announce myself, proudly, as a traditionalist. I am a product of that which is carpingly known as the 'old school', but I embrace the title. I have long considered that we do our young girls a disservice by insisting on all the psychology and technology (this is far better left to the medical men), instead of concentrating more on 'bottoms and bowels'. However, I digress. My reason for putting pen to paper is to take up cudgels

in defence of the traditional ward round which appears to be
disappearing all too swiftly from the scene.

There is, and I can say this without fear of contradiction, no
better way to liaise with our medical colleagues than this
traditional method. In my own ward I ensure that the tea and
toast are ready, piping hot, in my office, at 9.30 a.m. sharp. I do
not pretend that this is an indispensable plan of action — some
consultants prefer coffee, for instance — but on no account
should this necessary task be delegated to less experienced
members of staff, for assuredly they will not be a party to that
special relationship between you and your doctors. I have had
unhappy experiences in this regard; on one occasion the
atmosphere was ruined by one of my juniors (male, of course,
and thereby hangs a tale) inquiring quite insolently and, I fear,
not a little sarcastically, 'Shall I be mother?' For this reason I
consider myself to be the only appropriate nursing representative on the round, and any information that may be relevant to
nursing can be passed on at the right time by me.

While the medical staff are refreshing themselves, they are at
liberty to discuss specific cases, and items of general interest, in
a relaxed, unhurried atmosphere, for which, I think, they are
very grateful. As well as replenishing cups, and perhaps hand-
ing round biscuits, I find that I am often in a position to furnish
information about patients, which doctors find useful. To this
end I have my nurses complete what I jocularly call 'the bible',
which is a list of salient information about the patients. These
few extra minutes of nursing time are well spent, for on the
ward round busy doctors seldom have time to examine the
charts at the bottom of the bed.

It is as well to ensure that the nursing staff have all patients
on their beds before the start of the ward round, so all toileting
must really be out of the way by 9.00 a.m. Sometimes a round
extends beyond midday, and here more planning and fore-
thought are necessary. My own strategy is to postpone luncheon until convenient, and then provide sandwiches for patients
where meals are no longer available. In this way the vital
continuity of the ward round is preserved, and the exchange of
information (which, after all, is the point of the exercise) can
continue unhampered.

These are just a few of the guidelines for a profitable ward round which I have evolved over many years of experience. I hope others will benefit from them.

Admission

I have decided to devote this space to a discussion of the admission procedure; my remarks on the subject are intended primarily for the enlightenment of our younger girls, although even the more senior amongst my readers may benefit from a restatement of basic principles.

The admission procedure is the vital first contact between nurse and patient: it is crucial therefore that a good authoritative attitude is adopted from the outset, lest disciplinary problems ensue at a later stage.

Firstly, make sure the new patient dons night-wear as soon as possible after entry to the ward. This makes for much easier identification, and prevents the invalid from wandering about and interfering with the essential work of the ward.

Admission normally takes place outside visiting hours, so if there are any relatives in attendance they should be sent away with all convenient expedition. As I have remarked elsewhere, the interference from friends and family can be highly detrimental to the operation of the ward: before their departure, you must impress upon them the appropriate times for visiting, and exhort them not to telephone the ward at inconvenient times.

Give much thought to the positioning of the patient's bed. It is particularly undesirable to have young people placed together as they are apt to become frolicsome and mischievous in a way which can be disturbing to any senior medical staff who may be on the ward. As it is the aged who most frequently succumb to indispositions (an example of the contrary nature of old people), there is usually no problem in segregating youths by at least three beds.

A two-bed separation is normally enough to prevent normal conversation, but greater distances are to be preferred as young people seem to gain tremendous satisfaction from hurling objects at each other; this kind of horse-play cannot be endured as it is potentially injurious to other patients and staff. For this reason I always ensure that there are plenty of copies of the *Illustrated London News* and jigsaws to provide entertainment for the younger patient.

The admission procedure should be conducted as quickly as possible. The fiasco that was the Nursing Process was clear proof that we don't need to know about the person's life outside hospital. The ward is such a different environment from the patient's day-to-day surroundings, that there can be no possible benefit in delving into the various foibles and fascinations of the individual. Treat everybody the same and one cannot be accused of injustice.

In the days when we had a Nursing Process Co-ordinator, one of my proudest moments was to be congratulated on the fact that the only distinguishing feature on the admission forms of my patients was the name and telephone number. You see, illness is no respecter of the individual. It may strike rich and poor, male and female, good and bad. The experienced nurse will know that the bad have usually brought it upon themselves, but this need not concern us here.

Let's find out what the patient thinks is wrong with him, who his next of kin are and then get straight on to instructing him about ward routine. The times of meals, drinks, bowel rounds and the WRVS are the stuff of nursing admission. The medical staff will tell us what's wrong with the patient as soon as we need to know, and in the meantime, we should be getting on with the delivery of care.

So, your patient is on the ward, in bed and the paperwork is done. This should be accomplished in under 20 minutes and preferably within 15. Now is the time when the patient, recovering from his initial diffidence, will start to request information about his condition. Stand none of this.

It is unlikely that the doctor would wish to confide anything to the patient before consulting you, so it is perfectly honest to say that you don't know anything. When you do find out what the diagnosis is, consider carefully. Should the patient be told? You are, or soon will be, a trained nurse. You have grown accustomed to illness and disability. The patient is not so fortunately prepared.

While the term hallux valgus is commonplace to you, for the patient — who may not understand even simple Greek — the affliction is a metaphor for the transience of his own earthly existence. He may become hysterical. He may shout. He may even threaten to leave the ward. It is a sad comment on the times, but people are not as stoic in the face of adversity as they should be.

A firm yet non-committal response is the key to effective patient handling, and it may be of benefit to rehearse a short series of stock answers which may be resorted to when under pressure. 'I'm sure doctor knows best' and 'It's too early to tell' are two of my own favourites.

Having effectively staved off the requests for information, you move into the period of close observation which is the key to efficient nursing. Observe for signs of a limp which transfers from one side of the body to another; be alert for the sufferer who exhibits a healthy appetite; maintain vigilance for the tell-tale signs of a demanding or difficult personality. These are the sure signs of the malingerer. It is part of the unique function of the nurse to ensure that precious resources are not wasted on those who do not deserve them.

The genuinely afflicted are always quiet and co-operative. You may expect some slight groaning from those who are in the extremities of pain, but mistrust flamboyant displays of suffering that go beyond the bounds of good taste. The miracles of modern science have ensured that nowadays pain is largely kept within the limits of endurance and seldom increases beyond the level that we may describe as character-building.

It may be an unpopular contention but I am convinced that if people had to suffer a little *more* discomfort during their daily lives, our country would be the better for it. Let's stop wrapping our people in cotton wool, and let them feel the bracing and exhilarating knocks that life imparts as well as the pleasures. A man who has never lived in the cold does not appreciate the sun.

During your nursing career you will frequently be called upon to deal with the non-appearance of a patient. One's initial and justified reaction is to conclude that if the patient cannot be bothered to turn up on time, then he doesn't really deserve our consideration anyway. But one is forced, in the light of experience, to take a more liberal attitude. It is some very few weeks since a patient of mine was discovered in a neighbouring ward's waiting area, having been directed there by a particularly weak-headed medical student.

The patient had sat in the waiting room for some 9 hours before discovery; he was not unduly concerned, having been warned that patience was a necessary virtue in the modern hospital. I forget what was wrong with him, but he did say he wanted to take his case to an ombudsman. Regular readers will know that I do not believe in alternative therapies, especially those grounded in the black arts, so I was at pains to dissuade him from that course.

It must be remembered that the admission period can be a **highly traumatic** event. If you are to come through it with a modicum of calm, you must concentrate on the priorities of care and refuse to be diverted from the essential elements of the procedure.

You will still occasionally encounter the nurse tutor who, with introductory course nurse in tow, will spend some 2 or 3 hours interrogating the patient; you may rest assured that there will be nothing more to show for it than the invaluable information that he is a keen member of the bowls club and has a son in Australia.

The remedy for this nonsense is simple. Merely await the withdrawal of the inquisitors, tear up their 'care plans' and substitute a more appropriately completed form.

If we are resolute in our resistance to the unseemly interest in the patient's background, we may finally and triumphantly return to the business-like approach to admission that should be every nurse's aim!

Discharge

Having dealt in detail with the mechanics of admission, I now intend to give a few guidelines — based on a lifetime's experience — on the subject of discharge. These we may term the alpha and omega of patient care.

It is our duty to dismiss patients from the ward as soon as possible. There are many demands on our resources, and we must spare no efforts to clear our beds promptly and make room for the next wave of sick and needy, clamouring at our portals. The matter takes on even greater urgency of course, when we are waiting to admit patients under private care.

Judicial discharge can replace a non-paying invalid with one who creates wealth for the health service, rather than merely using up our resources. As we become increasingly accountable for the cost of the care we give, we must become aware of the profit and loss issues which underpin the care of the sick.

For the same reason, one must be wary of hastiness in sending the private patient home. He may well *seem* to be on the mend, but as we nurses know, what may appear as a recovery is all too often merely a remission in which the demon disease is restoring its powers in preparation for new outrages against the human frame. Therefore, if our medical superiors consider that a longer period of convalescence is demanded, we must support them, and give thanks for the fact that the patient is likely to make fewer demands on our time than the more seriously ill. In this regard, it is usually fairly easy to curtail routine admissions to smooth the path of the medical imperative.

But let me deal with discharge of the ordinary patient. To my mind, there is far too much energy and soul-searching wasted on fruitless investigations into the dischargee's home circumstances. The state of people's home circumstances is quite as irrelevant to the process of discharge as it is to admission.

To state the matter baldly, we know that the patient has come from home circumstances which were, at the very least, endurable. Through the good offices of professional surgeons and dedicated nurses (for such I hope you are) the patient will return home in better condition than when he arrived. Otherwise, what was the point of admitting him in the first place?

We as nurses need not be concerned with how many toilets he has. They were sufficient before, and will be in the future. Too many people nowadays believe that a short stay in hospital will give them a foot in the door of the welfare services. They expect *us* to provide costly apparatus, when this is the responsibility of their own families.

I am sorry to say that they are all too often aided and abetted in their fraudulent purposes by the Lady Almoner, or Medical

Social Worker, as she now insists on calling herself. Hardly a week passes without she arrives on my ward, clipboard in hand and ball-point pen a-quiver, interfering in the efficient and expeditious clearance of beds.

I tell her that it is impossible to predict who will be discharged: it is a matter of policy and good practice that patients are despatched at short notice. I have in the past tried to explain the good sense behind this philosophy, but in vain; therefore I usually confine my remarks to 'we don't have anybody for discharge just at the moment'. Then I can be sure of slipping a few out before her next visit.

It is my proud boast that most of my homeward-bound patients are well on their way before the busybodies get wind of it. I must confess it has become something of a game: pitting one's wits against the combined forces of the welfare department is a satisfying challenge.

A concomitant of the general moral decline of the nation has been the break-up of the family, and one sees evidence of this in relatives' reluctance to re-assume responsibility for the patient's care. We as nurses are continually beset by elements of the younger generation, talking about 'how difficult father has become'. As if we who have been waiting on him, hand and foot, didn't know it!

It is, and always has been, the responsibility of the family to look after their less resilient members, or find some suitable institution in which they can be kept out of harm's way. In dealing with difficult relatives, as with difficult patients, a firm approach is absolutely essential. Believe me, attempts to reason with them will only be interpreted as weakness.

Instead, remember the recommended approach to the Lady Almoner: discharge first and field their complaints afterwards! Once the patient is home, they'll have the utmost difficulty getting him back in again, the waiting lists being what they are. As I tell my girls in my lighter moments, possession is nine-tenths of the law. Once the family have got him, they keep him.

'Discharge with discretion' is the term I have coined to explain this approach to sending patients home. It does mean of course that one cannot rely on the family to provide transport, as they will ideally be unaware of what's going on until the happy sound of the doorbell signals the patient's return. That is why I cultivate a good relationship with our ambulance crews.

I would not usually seek to promote much intercourse between nurses and the ancillary services. Ambulancemen, for example, tend to clump about in heavy boots, are quite impertinent in their modes of address, and often attempt to smoke roll-up cigarettes in clinical areas. But they can move objects faster than Pickfords.

Give them all the help you can, that's my advice. Firstly ensure that all the patient's belongings are packed into stout polythene bags of routine issue. Do not allow the patient to collect his belongings under any circumstances. The level of pilfering from wards has reached epidemic proportions, and I have come across patients quite brazenly removing dressings and denture cartons from my ward. Clinical supplies are available from any reputable chemist at quite reasonable prices, and this should be impressed upon the patient.

Once all the property is bagged up, I place the patient in a wheelchair and insert the doctor's letter into some convenient pocket, along with any prescriptions for medications to be taken at home. Do not waste time scribbling out instructions to the district nurse: she will be told how to proceed by the GP.

My hospital has recently taken the enlightened step of providing us with some bright-yellow, self-adhesive stickers with the legend 'AMBULANCE' clearly printed in striking fluorescent letters. With one of these firmly positioned on the patient's forehead, there is little danger of his being mistaken for another patient while waiting for the ambulancemen. This excellent advance means that I no longer have to send escorting nurses down to the busy reception area in the main entrance hall of the hospital. A porter for the journey from the ward is all that is required.

The process of discharge is quite simple. There is a continuous need to empty beds. One may expect routinely tiresome resistance from relatives and the so-called welfare professionals. But, by the thoughtful application of the resources at your disposal, such difficulties may be minimised!

Borrowing

I am sure I am not alone in noting a significant increase in the level of borrowing between wards nowadays. Only yesterday I had to refuse a request — from a first-year student if you please — for a box of Glomerular capsules! In fact I know that I probably had a box or two in the drugs cupboard, but I absolutely refuse to lend out therapeutic chemicals under any circumstances. (I read with trepidation of pleas for nurses to be given prescribing powers. With correct safeguards, there is no reason why senior nurses should not continue to **dispense** medicines; medical staff are really too busy to have the burden of dispensing laid on them as well as that of prescribing. But we must be rigid in our practices and resist attempts to 'borrow' medications.) Instead, I directed nurse straight to the pharmacy: there is scarcely any ward situation which cannot be turned into a teaching opportunity, and I hope I am never too busy to contribute to the enlightenment of our young girls.

But examples of the insidious trend abound: every ward in my hospital originally possessed an electric fan, yet the number of requests for fans from other wards has reached an all-time high. Needless to say, I scarcely ever lend any of mine out. I have solved the 'walking apparatus syndrome' by clearly and indelibly marking all my equipment with the name of my ward for easy identification. (If you are thinking of adopting my strategy, I urge you to use a good quality permanent marker. I am loth to say it, but I am sure there are some Ward Sisters in my hospital who are not above erasing one name and inserting their own!)

At any moment one of my patients may become febrile and I must have the facilities to cope with emergencies as they arise. 'Plan for the worst' is a safe maxim. I direct petitioning staff from other wards to submit appropriate requisition forms to their Assistant Matron. Furthermore, if the nurse is of registered status, I point out, in no uncertain terms, that it is her responsibility to ensure that her ward is adequately stocked, not mine.

Electric fans are rather a Trojan horse of mine, yet there are many examples of this disturbing trend. Pleas for medication — even Schedule A drugs — are becoming more frequent. It ill behoves any nurse to attempt to rifle another's stock, merely because she has failed to procure sufficient supplies for her own pharmacy. One hears of the misuse of therapeutic chemicals, even by those held in the highest of public trust. My feelings for the Lakeland Poets have never been quite the same since learning that Samuel Taylor Coleridge was on drugs most of the time. In fact, I would counsel against the influence of poetry generally as poets often show evidence of an unstable humour. Shakespeare and Kipling excepted of course.

No, a ward is like a household, and must be run with a strict eye on incomings and outgoings. The insidious trend of borrowing to make ends meet must be halted, and our young girls trained in the techniques of good husbandry. A little joke I have with my girls is that to be good wives, they must be experts in husbandry! They are very amused by this little quip, but levity always has its serious side: a country, a home, a ward: none of them can survive if more is spent out than brought in. We have learnt to call it 'moneytarism', but it is really just good, old-fashioned common sense. When Hamlet said, 'Neither a lender, nor a borrower be. . .', he put his finger squarely on the nub of the matter.

Sometimes, though, the temporary loan of equipment is inevitable. A request from an Assistant Matron, or a member of the medical staff on behalf of a particularly serious case, must be met with a compassionate response; as a professional nurse, I cannot turn my back on suffering. But I do insist that my 'Emergency Loan Book' is duly completed with the name of the ward, the details of the article and the name of a member of the nursing staff from the ward concerned, to act as guarantor against its return. And when a ward does borrow an article from me, I fill out a requisition slip on their behalf for a similar item. When nurse collects our equipment, she gives Sister the requisition slip and a covering note from me to the effect that such borrowing is a drain on my resources, and I will not expect another such occurrence. This has been successful, by and large, and requests for loans are diminishing.

I should now share with my readers the fruits of my experience in the logistical control of the ward. Without doubt, one of the most difficult stock levels to maintain is that of linen.

I don't know what the laundry service is like at your hospital, but if it even approaches the rueful state of ours, I sympathise with you. Weekend after weekend my patients sleep wrapped in tissue paper like Gamage's glassware, and so short are we of even essential items such as pyjamas, I am even forced, occasionally, to allow my patients to wear their outdoor clothes during the day. Anybody who has noticed the growing fashion over the years for people — especially young people — to sleep in an unclothed state (what we in my training days called the 'shouldn't-be-seens') will share my disquiet. Quite apart from the greater incidence of self-induced pneumonia amongst these individuals, one shudders to think of the scenes if there were a fire or some other catastrophe necessitating nocturnal evacuation. I often have female patients well into their seventies on my ward, and can scarcely think they would react well to a cavalcade of shouldn't-be-seens rushing past, as their owners seek expeditious egress through the fire escapes. However, this is merely an antique thought.

As I say, it is extremely difficult to maintain adequate stocks of linen, especially over the weekend periods when laundry staff are happy to laze at home, while we maintain the care of our patients. Every Sunday afternoon, during a period of weekend cleaning, my senior staff nurse and I go out 'on manoeuvres' to other wards to look for surplus linen. You would scarce believe the attitude of some nurses to linen. I am convinced that many indulge in illicit hoarding, in plain contradiction of repeated memos from the Matron outlawing this practice. Pleas for a fresh drawer sheet or pillow case, however, invariably fall on deaf ears: there are none so deaf to the cries of the needy, in my experience, as those who won't hear. Fortunately there is usually sufficient linen lying unattended on the wards for our needs. I am always struck by how few nurses there are about on a Sunday afternoon, and this is of course lamentable, although beneficial to our purposes, particularly the re-stocking of my emergency contingency cupboard!

And one further word of caution: if you are about to set out on an expedition of reconnaissance of the sort I have described, be sure to leave a nurse out on your ward. This is not without its difficulties, given the other demands on nursing time at weekends, but it is worth the effort. There *are* nurses, obviously from the same school of thought as those who tamper with the labelling of apparatus, who exploit periods of low staffing levels to steal equipment from undefended wards. The guilty in my own hospital know whom it is that I am referring to, but I am sure such vipers nest in the bosom of every hospital. Be warned, lest you return to your ward to find your cupboards bare.

Following the admirable Mr Sainsbury's review of Health Service Management, which I have already written in support of elsewhere, nurses are to become more fundamentally responsible for the resource management of their wards. It has long been my contention that any fool — even a first-year student — can feed and water a patient, but it takes a registered nurse to ensure that the ward is supplied with all the necessaries, whether it be coffee for the doctors or egg white for bed sores. The challenge of ward organisation is a great one; let us not flinch from it!

Tidiness

Ward presentation is a matter that receives insufficient attention in basic nurse training, yet it is one of vital importance. In line with the general decline in nursing standards, there is now a sense that our surroundings do not matter. They do.

A tidy ward is an efficient ward, and I always ensure that a major portion of the day is dedicated to correcting the disarray which patients — by their very nature — invariably create. It is a source of constant wonder to me that people who are ill, and therefore immobile, can cause havoc in my ward in the brief space between evening and morning.

Fortunately, I have evolved systems that restore order and peace to the environment, and I am sure that many of our younger girls will profit from a brief résumé of my approach.

Nothing makes a ward seem more of a slum than unmade beds and disorganised bed areas. While I am taking a brief handover report from the night staff, my nurses set out with the linen trolley on the bed-making round. It seems that the correct approach is no longer taught in the school of nursing, and so I always give new probationers a short course in 'the right way to do it'. I impress upon them the importance of 'The Forearm Rule'. This vital rudiment, which has been handed down to us from Florence Nightingale, states that the sheet must be turned back over the counterpane, so that it extends the same length as that between the elbow and wrist.

Some years ago, a particularly impertinent nurse, who has thankfully left the profession, argued that as nurses' forearms varied in length, there would always be some departure from uniformity. Personally, I think that would-be nurses whose limbs display aberrant proportions should be winkled out at the entrance medical, but in the meantime I have hit upon an expedient which silences all know-alls. I have refined Nightingale's original directive to 'Sister's Forearm Rule'.

Now, at the start of each ward allocation, I encourage probationers to measure their forearms against a life-size photographic representation of mine, which is permanently displayed in my office.

At first, they are required to draw small ink marks on the underside of their arms, but as they get the knack of it, they are able to dispense with such graphic references. As a result, the beds present an enchanting prospect to the eye, with a uniform white stripe extending along the ward.

Attention to detail is what distinguishes the good nurse, and by 9 a.m. — when I make my tour of inspection — I expect the beds to be pristine. If for any reason they fall below standard, then I insist that the beds are stripped and the process begun again from the start. By resolutely ensuring the very highest standards, my girls learn quickly and well. They will not be slapdash if they know I am ceaselessly vigilant for lapses. Once the beds are made to my satisfaction, we may move on to the next vital stages of the morning's work. Lockers.

I like to start the locker round while patients are eating their breakfasts. One can tell so much about the moral fibre of the patient by the state of his personal effects, and I lose no opportunity as a health educator to lecture the invalid on the importance of 'running a tight ship'.

Each locker is emptied and checked for untoward items such as used tissues, confectionery, and those arch enemies of order, the get-well cards. The first two are discarded immediately, but mine is not a heart of stone, and I do not insist that greeting cards are thrown away. Instead, I provide a brown paper bag in which such cards can be stored — in my office — until the patient's discharge.

I also discourage relatives from bringing flowers on to my ward. Flowers are not just untidy, they are positively dangerous. In their place, the WRVS has been kind enough to furnish me with a selection of attractive and cheerful plastic chrysanthemums, which are easily cleaned with a moist cloth and dilute phenolic solution.

In case my more perspicacious readers think I have forgotten something, I haven't. On my ward, denture cartons are kept in the sluice until denture round time at 10.30 a.m. A senior nurse is detailed to clean all the dentures at once, which is a much more effective use of time, before redistributing them. Even with this simple arrangement, it's amazing how often we end up with a spare top plate or two. I now have an impressive collection of surplus dentures, which come in very useful when elderly patients neglect to bring their own into hospital with them. We can always find something to fit!

While we are on the subject of sluices, I have always maintained that one can tell how good the nurses are by the state of the 'engine room' of the ward. Thanks to my resistance to the disgusting fashion for disposable paper bed-pans and urinals, we are still the proud owner of a 1936 Armstrong Stroud

Hydromatic Bedpan Washer, a living tribute to the golden age of ancillary engineering. This solid machine has given our hospital 40 years of trouble-free service, apart from the occasional explosive decompression. I shall return to sluice management in a future treatise, but in the meantime I exhort all my readers to re-examine their priorities and concentrate on producing ward areas of which we can really be proud!

Visiting

Of all the periods in the hospital day, Visiting Time must be one of the most pressurised and least satisfactory for the busy nurse. We all have good reason to regret the extension in visiting hours foisted upon us by misguided theorists!

If a systematic approach to medical and nursing care is to be maintained, the random and counter-productive interferences from relatives must be strictly controlled.

Time and time again, I have been interrupted in important ward administration duties by visitors asking for extra glasses of water, additional blankets, or information about treatment and prognoses. Invariably they fail to understand that as the person most closely involved with the patient, *I* should be the one to decide whether a patient needs a drink or not.

The number of visitors who seem to have no conception of the importance of fluid balance charts is amazing. Only last week, I had an old man on my ward from one of the European countries, Denmark or Germany or somewhere; needless to say, his command of English left much to be desired. He pestered me all day for extra drinks of water, which I staunchly refused in accordance with explicit instructions from the doctor to limit fluid intake. Doctor had not confided the rationale for this decision to me, but once a course of action has been prescribed, it is my professional duty to carry it out.

Needless to say, within minutes of the onset of Visiting Hour, I was surrounded by members of the patient's family, brandishing his empty water jug and jabbering away twenty to the dozen.

Like Coriolanus, I will have no truck with the mob. Singling out a senior member of the group who demonstrated a little more mental agility than the rest, I explained in easily comprehensible terms that doctor had said that the patient was not *allowed* to drink. Light dawned eventually and the group were persuaded to return to the bedside. I gave the matter no thought (besides making a 'difficult patient' entry in the Kardex with one of my self-adhesive red stars) until my customary inspection of the patient charts prior to evening handover.

Leafing through the fluid balance charts, I found one with no entries since the early afternoon. I don't need to tell the more perspicacious amongst my readers whose chart it was. Taking my instructions *literally*, the stupid man had steadfastly refused to drink, and was supported in his resolve by his family, quoting me as their authority. Consequently 6 hours had passed without oral refreshment, bringing the patient to the brink of a dehydration necessitating intravenous infusion: if only relatives didn't interfere, such inconveniences could be avoided.

There is, however, a positive postscript to this fluid limitation issue: it transpired that the restriction was imposed mistakenly, following a misunderstanding of purpose between house officer and registrar, so the patient could return to free fluids from the following morning anyway. Or at least, he could have done were he not going to theatre in the afternoon.

The fact that should be made clear to all individuals visiting patients is that nurses and doctors know what they are doing, and that interference is only likely to confuse and complicate matters.

The same applies to the matter of talking to visitors about patients' conditions in general. Many of my younger girls have picked up the idea, no doubt from some fad-swallowing tutor from the School of Nursing, that what the anxious relative needs most of all is a detailed analysis of the sufferer's condition. Balderdash!

If they wish to know about medical conditions, members of the public will find ample reference materials in any good local library, or if they are that interested, they can train as nurses themselves. We already have far too much to do to be providing free seminars on pathology and microbacteriology to people who forget it all straight away anyway.

For most visitors (doctors' relatives excluded of course), a simple condition check such as, 'We're very pleased with him', or 'He's as well as can be expected, all things considered', is quite sufficient. Delving into intricate detail gives the impression that the patient and his condition are something remarkable when, in fact, it is likely that the same condition passes through our wards twenty times a year.

In extremis, if a family is especially importunate of information, it is acceptable to refer them to medical staff who have received special training in deflecting difficult enquiries. It must none the less be borne in mind that if every visitor has such an interview with the doctor, he will never have time to do any real doctoring!

If there is any particularly bad news to be passed on then the doctor must be called in to inform the relatives, although the nurse carries the responsibility for identifying the right relative. This is very important.

I had a very regrettable experience in this regard recently, owing to an administrative blunder by a ward clerk over the matter of a pile of notes: the family having been assembled in the office by myself, our house officer solemnly informed the family group that he did not expect their father to last the night.

A shocked silence was succeeded by hysteria, wailing and gnashing of teeth, and a number of other emotional excesses which I thought — until then — were the sole domain of the Hispanic peoples. It transpired that the distressed family had come to visit their mother who, having made a full recovery from some minor surgical procedure, was packing her bags prior to discharge. As far as they knew, the male head of the family was, even as we spoke, digging over potatoes on his corporation allotment.

Fortunately, I was able to carry off the situation by administering a stern lecture on the dangers of allowing elderly people to over-exert themselves in horticultural activity, and that they should view this misunderstanding as a warning.

I don't know what it is about children, but they seem pathologically incapable of conducting themselves with any decorum in the presence of sick and dying people. Within moments of arrival they are to be found bouncing on *occupied* beds, playing with trolleys, or clambering over the hapless invalid. I was always taught that children under the age of 14 should not be allowed into clinical areas, and on the few occasions when I have transgressed this rule, I have regretted it. Deeply.

Mine is not a heart of stone, however: in the case of close family, some provision must be made. In my ward I am fortunate to have a glass panel between the visitors' waiting room and the ward itself. Children are thus free to wave at their uncle or father through the glass, who in turn — if they are possessed of any imagination whatsoever — may entertain them with risible tricks, such as the juggling of grapes or humorous charades.

What must be resisted at all costs is the heretical view that hospital can, or should be, made like home. Visitors must realise that hospitals are business-like places where extravagant emotional behaviour is out of the question. The rigour of the good hospital routine is a great impetus for the sufferer — psychologically speaking — to get better swiftly. With the kind of hotel atmosphere that 'the moderns' wish to impose, it is unlikely that invalids or their relatives would ever go home!

No, my advice is to keep Visiting Time to 1 hour of well-regulated activity a day and thus ensure that truly professional care is interrupted as little as possible. The welfare of our patients is at stake!

2 Of National Moment

Today, the major issues facing the nursing profession are much more likely to find their way into the national media, attracting the customary hysteria and misrepresentation as they go.

Fortunately for us, Angela Plume has never been afraid to confront the most thorny political and social questions of our time. By applying simple common sense she deflates rhetoric, punctures pretensions, and confounds her opponents.

Each of the following pieces shows Miss Plume at her incisive and analytical best; together they offer a dispassionate overview of modern nursing history.

The Griffiths Report

Whilst I have had my reservations about the standard — and standards — of student nurses arriving on the wards, I must say that my current crop of girls are certainly a cut above what we have been forced to accept as average. The facts speak for themselves: two out of the group already engaged to be married to members of our medical staff (albeit junior ones), and another sharing an 'understanding' with a prominent member of our local Round Table Group who may yet, I believe, stand for parliament.

Consequently I leant an indulgent ear to some of my girls when they asked me, recently, 'What about the Griffiths Report,

Sister Plume?' Readers will know that I am one who is mainly concerned with the essential 'nuts and bolts' of our calling, and usually have little time for philosophical musings about management science and all that kind of nonsense. There are already more than enough people in our Profession who contemplate their navels at the slightest provocation, and I have no intention of identifying with them!

None the less, as a Ward Sister, I am viewed as a representative of authority, and my subordinates are often pleased to seek my views on a wide range of subjects, thus reaping the benefits of a senior nurse's experience. This is only natural, and I think it is far better that my girls form their opinions on the basis of informed criticism from me than being influenced by Trades Unionists, radicals and others who revel in half-baked ideologies.

Thus it was that my researches led me to the pages of the *Nursing Times*; having consulted past editions (particularly November 23rd–29th 1983), I find myself able to share some thoughts and reflections on the whole management debate.

As evidenced by the uncertainty of the young nurses, there seems to be widespread concern, even panic, about the so-called Griffiths Report. Yet this is not a new phenomenon: as long ago as November 23rd 1983, nurses were worried about these proposals. And what has happened? **Nothing**, of course! I speak as one who has lived and worked through many structural changes in the National Health Service, and my words of comfort are precisely these: though the heavens may rage with argument yea and nay, the situation on the wards remains basically unchanged. This is, of course, a tribute to the perennial values of the Nursing Profession which spans generations in a unique manner. No profession has maintained a hold on tradition and traditional values as successfully as has nursing, and that — fundamentally — is why I am still proud to call myself a nurse.

Now, let us not be mistaken; there are things lamentably wrong with the Profession which may only be corrected by determined action. These aberrations occur only when radicals and intelligentsia are allowed to tamper with the true ethos of nursing. I strongly advocate vigilance against any such movements (viz., changes in Nurse Education, Nursing Process,

Americans, etc., etc.), but I am confident that they will finally be repulsed.

But let me turn to the issues involved in a little more detail: the appointment of General Managers does not seem to me, of itself, a bad idea. I know as a Ward Sister that any organisation needs a firm hand on the tiller — **one** firm hand! Rule by committee always leads to one thing: Anarchy. They set out to design a horse and end up with a five-legged giraffe!!

It is of course no surprise to those of us at the 'business end' of the Health Service that there has been a rush of claims for positions as General Managers from administrators, accountants, shop-keepers and the like. Sensing a gravy train, they all want to leap aboard. But, **back to basics**! Where were the accountants and administrators during the Crimean War? Doctors and nurses are the only people involved centrally in the provision of medical care and they share a unique relationship. This has been the case since the formation of our profession, under the guns of the enemy.

It would not be fitting for our two Professions to be seen wrangling in the public eye. My own suggestion, which I intend to put before the relevant authorities, is that the General Managers should be drawn from the ranks of our most respected Consultant Medical staff. They, having already achieved the summit of success and influence, will undertake the posts for the best of motives, far removed from petty ambition. In addition, they should be supported in this role by assistants who have proved their worth in the field of clinical nursing over the years.

This partnership would reflect the singular relationship which exists between the two professions and will work just as effectively as it does in the wards and out-patient departments of our hospital, where the nurse supports her doctor in his work.

Only recently I have been able to witness for myself the symmetry and decorum of nurse and doctor working in harmony within our very own Orthopaedic Out-patients Department. My visit was part of some lunatic initiative in which senior nurses are supposed to gain insight into the work of other departments. (Essentially misguided: if I wanted to drive an ambulance or work in a laundry, I would have done so, but we may let that pass.)

I was struck by the excellent organisation of the department which was certainly a tribute to Sister's influence: when a patient was brought in to see the Consultant, Nurse was on hand to show him a seat. Then she would stand quietly behind Mr Linnet's chair, ready to pass him his patella hammer, or other apparatus, as necessary. Should the patient interrupt the distinguished surgeon, Nurse was able to offer a gentle reproof — 'Sshh dear, let Doctor finish!' — before ushering him out when the Consultant pronounced himself satisfied.

This business-like approach, and sound understanding between nurse and doctor, meant that Mr Linnet was able to see some 40 patients before luncheon, and attend to some of his many commitments outside the hospital in the afternoon.

It can readily be seen that each member of the management pair in my system will be in a position to reach objective conclusions about policy, but the nurse will also be able to give a woman's view of the situation — the soft touch to the diplomacy of decision-making.

This is a realistic solution to the management problem. Accountants and Administrators no doubt have their part to play, but not, I am afraid, as General Managers. This role is better left to those who are at the heart of the National Health Service; in the warp and weft as it were. I proclaim myself ready to answer such a call were it made, although I would be reluctant, of course, to leave the bedside.

If this solution is not acceptable, then I would recommend leaving things as they are. As I tell my girls on the ward, change seldom means improvement, and often heralds a decline. Those of us who *have* lived through previous changes suspect that reorganisations serve merely as pastimes for underemployed intellectuals and bureaucrats.

We all know, deep down, that the current trend for presenting management as a mysterious pseudo-profession is folly. Management is something we do as a matter of course, while doing a hundred-and-one other things. I myself have never received any 'training' in management, yet I function quite effectively. When there is a Royal College of Managers, then, perhaps, we should start to worry about the Griffiths Report. Until then, let us forget the diversion of management sciences and concentrate on our primary role!

Shift Changes

I feel that the subject of the proposed shift changes — for some time the subject of animated and quite unnecessary debate — deserves some summarising comment from me to put things in their true perspective. Now, let it not be said that I am automatically opposed to change as a matter of principle: if it can be demonstrated that there is no threat to the essential fabric of this great Profession of ours, a new approach can often provide a welcome breath of fresh air through the portals of a stagnant system.

When I was first appointed as Sister to my present ward, many years ago, I saw myself very much in the role of 'a new brush', and lost no time in re-organising our patterns of work into a more business-like and efficient system. Those decisions have been vindicated by the passage of some 20 years, during which time no further adjustment to my original system has been necessary!

So, if some of my colleagues are in any way resistant to change, I would say to them, 'Remember, the present shift system has not always been with us!' (It is as well to remind our younger girls of this too!) When I joined the Profession, shifts were very much longer and consequently our leisure hours more limited. This did not put us out of countenance one whit: we were all following our vocation and expected to make certain sacrifices. Nay, we rejoiced in those sacrifices, for they were tangible proof of our dedication.

I do not necessarily recommend a return to the working conditions of yesteryear; apart from other considerations I would anticipate rabid opposition from the Trades Unions. Moreover, the provision of an overlap period between shifts has proved of particular value to me as a Ward Sister: there are many little jobs around the ward which are more easily completed at a time of increased staffing, when there are many untrained and student nurses to be occupied. As any good housekeeper will tell you, her work is never done! There are always shelves to be tidied and equipment to be cleaned, and I have been able to move these necessary tasks out of the realm of rushed weekend cleaning and spread them across the week in a more even and effective manner. Junior nurses find this work valuable because they learn quickly where items are stored around the ward, and can more easily become *au fait* with ward routine.

I have written elsewhere about the virtues of a traditional training approach. Florence Nightingale's probationers combined diverse housewifely duties with the provision of bedside comfort. They could as easily turn their hands to fire-lighting or scrubbing the floors as to soothing the fevered brow: they were all-rounders in every sense of the term. In these days of oil-fired central heating and ancillary staff, the nurse is no longer as fundamentally responsible for the 'whole patient', and this is to be regretted. None the less, the essence of these duties can be recreated in ward-cleaning activities such as polishing suction machines and cataloguing the linen cupboards, and I give my young girls plenty of this kind of experience. I tell them that they must learn to walk before they can run. (This is, of course, only a figure of speech: nobody runs on my ward unless there is an emergency such as a cardiac arrest or an unexpected visit by one of the Consultants!)

No nurse learns about complex technicalities such as intravenous infusions or bandaging until they have scored more than 90% in my 'Where-Does-It-Live?' quiz which I run every fortnight. And once they *have* graduated to bedside practice, woe betide them if they then forget where anything lives!

Now, tell me! How would I have time for such a comprehensive system of training, (Programmed Learning I believe it is called, nowadays!) if the overlap in shifts is phased out?

I have also described elsewhere the importance of properly organised medical ward rounds. It is desirable that these should be carried out at a time when I can leave another qualified nurse to run the ward whilst I participate in the essential business of the round. The removal of the overlap would undoubtedly cause inconvenience to the medical staff; I would not be able to give Doctor my full concentration were I to be forced into the position of leaving untrained staff out on the ward.

I have read reports of the introduction of 12-hour shifts to certain hospitals. As I have said, such working periods would not be new to me; none the less, we should be wary of any system which has its origins in America, as I suspect this one does. The Americans — or 'our friends from across the water' as I call them in light-hearted moments — are very fond of exporting their theories to us; I am convinced that they see England as a testing-ground for every new bizarre idea they hatch. The more disastrous the results, the more amusement they derive from us! But do we tell them we'll have none of it? No! We persist in our infatuation with all things American, while they chuckle and cackle on into the night, warming their hands at a fire fuelled by Nursing Process forms. Who would guess that we invented nursing in the first place?

No, let us keep the overlap, which has brought benefit to nurses and doctors alike. Most of all, let us have confidence in the English way of doing things, and ensure that our Great Profession is not blown hither and thither on the breeze of American whim.

I am well aware that in a time of economic recession nurses must be seen to lead the way in giving value for money and to strive for improvement in this area. But I do not believe the best way to do this is changing long-established and well-tried shift systems. We must instead promote an attitude in our young girls which moves away from a rigid interpretation of starting and finishing times. It must be made clear to new entrants to the profession that shift times are for guidance only, and that they must accept the realities of regularly working overtime. If we really wish to be considered a Profession, we must put our patients first and leave clock-watching to production-line workers. This may, at first, seem idealistic but that first impression is the product of prevailing attitudes of our time which have not always been thus. Professional status can be regained, but only if a concerted effort is made by the Schools of Nursing and Matrons alike!

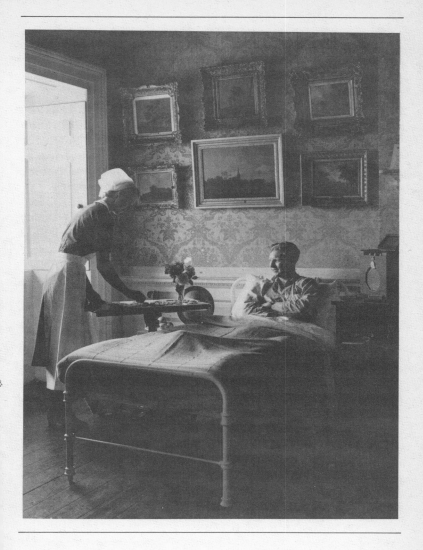

Nurse Training

I have followed, with increasing horror, the debate on the future of Nurse Training. It seems to me that there is a fashion for taking established and well-tried systems and tinkering with them — to their detriment!!

And to what end, may I ask? Recently, the 'change-for-change-sake lobby', as I call them, have overstepped the mark, demanding changes that are as impractical as they are sweeping. Such nonsense! And more disquieting when it is realised that they come from once well-respected bodies such as the RCN and GNCC. One begins to suspect **systematic infiltration** by revolutionaries, so well entrenched do they seem. In my day these kinds of aspirations would have been condemned as **radical** . . . and quite right too!! We had no truck with such doctrines, and never confused mere **change** with **progress**.

What of this supposed crisis in Nurse Education? No such crisis exists, in my mind. For instance, the so-called wastage rate amongst our young girls is quite clearly a method of natural selection or, as I am fond of saying, a means by which the sickly twig may be rent from the healthy bough.

Interviews cannot achieve perfect selection, and it is one of my main beliefs that too much emphasis on high academic qualifications has resulted in more nurses arriving on the wards who are basically unsuited to the demands of our work. Far better is it that such individuals are allowed to see their mistake and move to some less demanding occupation (a Lady Almoner, for example), rather than soldier on to the embarrassment of their colleagues and disadvantage of their patients. I might add that academic distinction was never my forte. Need I say more?

The practical nature of our great work is — I believe — central to the issue: sociologists and educationalists (teachers surely?) would have us believe, dear reader, that nursing can be learnt at a Polytechnical College. Such arrant nonsense! We, the silent majority of this great Profession of ours, know this. Do we require diplomas to wipe our patients' bottoms? Indeed, if our typical patient was ever consulted, he would certainly reject the over-qualified intellectual, with her eyes fixed — not upon the bedpan — but on some distant management post. As it happens I don't believe in overmuch consultation with patients, as all my girls know. Fussing round the invalid with information about this, and questions about that, merely adds to his burden. He will find much more security in a business-like relationship with an authoritative nurse. Nurse knows best, subject to the overall wisdom of the Ward Sister of course. But I digress.

Yes, our patient — if he were consulted — would reject the girl with her mind crammed full of learning and welcome the State Enrolled Nurse, the practically trained and practically minded girl, whom the profession has always attracted. And yet, what do we read? That enrolled nurse training is to be phased out!

Let my readers cast their minds back to the origins of the Nursing Profession and Florence Nightingale. When establishing her great training schools, she did not search the groves of academe for likely novices. No, her nurses of the future were to be working girls, accustomed to physical labour and of a sound constitution. They would accept the discipline and privations of their vocation without a thought, and rejoice in the satisfaction of a job well done. And if their intelligence was not of the first rank, then this was more than compensated by a sound, earthy common sense.

If there is to be any adjustment to our system of Nurse Training, let it be an increased emphasis on the Nightingale Philosophy. Florence Nightingale's training methods **were** the best available and still are, to my mind. When all the domestic chores were completed, and the patients quiet, she would draw her probationers into a circle about her chair and entertain them with instructive anecdotes gleaned from her experience in the Crimea. This is the way girls learn best: from first-hand instruction based on the knowledge of an older — and wiser — nurse. Miss Nightingale had no need of textbooks from America, or Audio/Visual apparatus; she didn't have them! She taught from experience, and my goodness, they learnt.

Yet today, young learners lack the essential respect for the past to a degree that is outrageous. A young person who can greet a reminiscence of a senior nurse with the words, 'But things have changed since those days, Sister Plume', has no place in the Profession as far as I am concerned. I am encouraged, however, by reports from some of my students that many of our Nurse Tutors are still standing up for tradition, and continuing to base all their teaching on anecdotal instruction.

As I have watched our working week reduced over the years to the present $37\frac{1}{2}$ hours (part-timers did more than this in my day!), I have seen a decrease in the occupational satisfaction of this once proud profession of ours. And though it may offend some to say it — say it I must — the standard of work has followed a similar progressive deterioration.

This is not entirely the fault of the young girls involved; most of those I come into contact with seem to come from good families, by and large, and once taught the correct way to proceed, show a rapid improvement. But my point is that the general environment in which the young learners spend their formative years is not conducive to the establishment of the right attitudes. And make no mistake, the right attitudes are **vital**! If you give individuals the right kind of leadership, you will soon bear the fruits of an efficient and committed workforce.

If readers are tempted to cavil at my traditional approach, then consider: what are the nurses' main topics of conversation nowadays? I remember well that our moments of leisure were often occupied with speculation and argument about the welfare and prognoses of our various patients. Walking back to the Nurses' Home we would exchange anecdotes and revel in the comradeship of our shared task.

Now, night-clubs, pop music, and anticipation of the next set of days off seem to be the only subjects worthy of interest. Attempts to engage nurses in stimulating conversation are met with such rejoinders as, 'I don't discuss that out of work'.

It has been argued that the reduction in working hours and the increase in salaries have attracted the wrong kind of people into the profession. This must be true to a degree: it is obvious to me that the vast influx of people who are only in the profession because of enhanced financial rewards must be a sorry development for nursing as a whole. But it is also true that promising entrants are led astray by the prevailing philosophies and fashions. Consider this: the community spirit of nursing which provided me with support *and* diversion has been steadily eroded. Nurses' Homes sold, longer leisure hours, and more disposable income all militate against the *esprit de corps* which was our bulwark in times gone by.

I firmly believe that nothing will be achieved by tinkering with the present training system. Our present predicament

demands a resolute approach from all concerned parties, oppos-
ing the sale of Nurses' Homes and all other measures which
seek to equate nurses with other members of the community.
We *are* different. We *are* special. And we must make that clear
by demonstrable evidence of our dedication. Words such as
Vocation, Commitment, Duty: how unfashionable they are
now! But it will not always be so. Laxity is always self-defeating
(witness the Roman Empire), and is eventually supplanted by a
system of truly perennial values. This being the case, I call upon
all right-minded members of the profession to stand up and be
counted!

Project 2000

And so, the debate about Project 2000 remains, according to the
Nursing Times, 'as heated as ever'. Let me say at the outset that
most of my girls are under the impression that Project 2000 is
one of those misguided initiatives, so beloved of youth organi-
sations, in which household artefacts are placed in a biscuit tin
and buried, in the hope that they will be dug up again, and
marvelled over by future generations. Would that this was the
case. As far as I am concerned, the sooner — and
deeper — Project 2000 is buried, the better.

I had hoped to let this latest hobby-horse die from the
flogging of its own supporters as the Nursing Process did, but
once again I have been forced to put pen to paper before we are
completely engulfed by a flood of propaganda issuing from
those who wish to see an American system imposed on the
Profession. They shall not pass!

Let us consider the facts. We are, quite rightly, increasingly
accountable for our use of resources. I have always said that as
the most dedicated of the professions (apart from medicine), we
must be seen to lead the way in giving 'value for money'. At the
same time, sensationalist articles have appeared in all the
popular media, agonising over the wastage rate amongst students and qualified nurses.

We are also told that owing to the explosion in birth control,
and the fact that women are forsaking the home and hearth,
there are not enough young females of suitable character and
background to enter the profession. (I don't believe this myself.

I know of at least five good families with daughters whose lack of matrimonial prospects makes them eminently suitable for careers in nursing. However . . . .)

This then is the position: not enough nurses and scarce resources. And what is the GNCC's solution to this so-called crisis? Project 2000, an ingenious scheme which will remove 85,000 student nurses from the wards, closely followed by the SENs. And nobody knows how much this will all cost. Excellent!

I have already given my views on the direction nurse training should take in the future. Despite many letters of support from the silent majority of nurses who make up my readership, the powers-that-be have elected to ignore my contribution. So be it. They will have cause for regret soon enough.

It seems nurse training is now far too important to happen on the wards. Let us take our probationers to fire stations, employment exchanges, local government offices, anywhere as long as they don't come into contact with people who have unpleasant diseases and complaints. After all, say the socialists, you can't expect the new-style nurse to stand for parliament, strike, or become a sociology professor if she is surrounded by sick people all the time, can you?

I blame the men. They joined the profession against the wishes of our own professional body, took power, and then decided that nursing wasn't really what they wanted to do. Not possessed of the simple decency to leave, they must needs change nursing beyond all recognition, until it **does** meet their conception of a profession.

But the Schools of Nursing are equally culpable. It should come as no surprise that Educationalists are in favour of Project 2000. My own School of Nursing boasts more communists than the BBC; mark my words, people who have forsaken the bedside once will welcome any measure that distances them still further from ward-based activity.

I've seen them at work. They are never happier than when encouraging learners to 'feel each other's space' or 'verbalise their internal conflicts'. What disgusting suggestions. How about teaching aseptic technique, or respect for one's betters?

Less than a week ago, whilst on an errand from my ward, I chanced to glance into one of the lecture theatres to see students playing what can only be described as charades. Their tutor (who first came to my notice last Spring when I was the victim of an outrage that masqueraded as an April Fool's Day stunt) trained in the North of England and one has to make certain allowances, but as the whole class was clearly out of control, I decided to take charge of the situation.

Singling out the ring-leaders, I sent them to stand outside Matron's office, while directing the remaining students to apply themselves to their anatomy books. When I left, the class was completely silent, and I could see that several of the students were deeply moved by the lead I had shown, almost to the point of tears.

I have since received a courteous note from Matron thanking me for my timely intervention. The tutor had tried to rationalise the anarchy in his classroom by saying that it was a 'role-playing exercise' or some such nonsense, but this cut no more ice with Matron than it would have done with me.

Learners have, since the beginning of the Profession, made a useful contribution to the work of the ward. It is probably not going too far to say that, on one or two occasions, I may have been hard put to cope without them. More importantly, whilst they laboured in useful and character-building tasks, they were prepared for greater responsibility. They learnt to respect doctors; they learnt how to spot the malingerer; they learnt the importance of routine and how to be cruel to be kind. All this will end at a stroke.

Let us follow the learner to qualification and beyond. Having received her certificate (no mention of the return of the State Badge despite outcries from the Profession, I notice), she reports to her first ward with approximately the same amount of useful knowledge as an introductory course nurse, and yet she is to be the registered practitioner. Registered practiser would be a more appropriate nomenclature. I am confident that disaster will ensue, for both the ward and the individual nurse.

People complain now that nurses leave the Profession after only 18 months. But where is the problem? At least we've had nearly 5 years' work out of them, and time to train another lot. In future we'll be lucky to keep them for 18 weeks, and nothing to show for all the 'education' lavished upon them.

Of course, when change is to be instituted, the patients are the very last people to be consulted. But the *Nursing Times* is not the only authority to conduct research into the responses to

Project 2000. And I went to the people who really matter. I have recently completed a straw poll amongst my patients, and I can announce that a group of people differing widely in age and pathology were united in their total confidence in the present system.

In answer to my objective questions, they pronounced themselves unanimously against any system which threatened the very fabric of the Nursing Profession. So much for the mystique surrounding research. It holds no terrors for me, even if I did train in the good old days when asking questions was considered impertinent.

You may be sure that one source of revenue for Project 2000 will no doubt be the iniquitous new fee system. Legalised extortion, readers, is what it is. When I paid seventeen-and-six (2 weeks' wages) to be admitted to the register all those years ago, I did so on the understanding that I was admitted for life. We are being swindled, and the booty used to destroy what is left of the Profession.

There is a solution. I call upon all like-minded individuals to join in a movement with me to resist the changes, protect the Profession and vanquish those who would impose their views on us. The new organisation will take as its title Project 1860; if the significance of this date escapes some of my younger readers, I would direct them to their history books. Project 1860 will be the rallying point for all those nurses who believe that the professional principles espoused by Florence Nightingale are worth fighting for. Down with the modernists!

Recruitment Crisis

I had hoped to deliver a thought-provoking treatise on the operation and maintenance of the Armstrong Stroud Bedpan Washer, but affairs of national moment have intervened; it seems that one can hardly open one's newspaper, turn on one's wireless, or indeed leaf through one's *Nursing Times*, without being assailed by hysterical outpourings concerning the so-called recruitment crisis. If we are to believe the whingers and sensationalists, the care of the nation's sick is currently in the hands of seven or eight introductory-course nurses who are all homeless, malnourished and prey to an affliction which is described by the Americans as 'meltdown' or 'burn-up' or some such. All rubbish of course, but I have none the less exercised my mind on the subject of recruitment in an effort to set the Profession's mind at rest. Had the delegates seen fit to elect me to the Council of the GNCC in Glasgow, the following proposals would probably already be on their way to implementation, but I am not one to bear grudges.

Firstly, if we are to encourage an increased volume of applications for nurse training from suitable young girls, we must address our attentions to their parents. These are the people who will ultimately decide the career of their offspring and we must not rest until they are aware of the advantages of having a nurse in the family. These may seem self-evident to my readers, but they are well worth re-stating:

1. Nurse training is an ideal and unique rounding-off to a young woman's education, providing a smooth transition between childhood and motherhood.
2. The student nurse is brought into contact with a large number of highly eligible young men amongst the junior medical staff, and there are thus increased opportunities to contract an advantageous matrimonial alliance.
3. Owing to the huge increases in allowances paid to nurses over the last decade (wholly ill-advised to my mind), nurses now command an income that far exceeds their wants: with appropriate guidance, much of the surplus may be channeled back into the family to comfort the ageing parents in their declining years.
4. Where advancing age incapacitates the parents, the daughter is better equipped to minister to their needs, thus saving the State unnecessary expense, and freeing other members of the family from encumbering responsibilities.

These few points should convince parents that putting their daughter into the Health Service is an honourable and seemly course to follow. Having guaranteed a sympathetic audience among the older generation, the authorities must ensure that the nation's youth, from primary school age onwards, are educated in the ethics of caring and self-sacrifice.

In recent years this has been sadly neglected. It may surprise my readers to know that there are now children who are growing up in ignorance of the admirable Sue Barton books; today in our schools, girls are encouraged to waste their time on mathematics and metal work, while such instinctive strengths as nurturing and cookery are ignored and allowed to atrophy. Much work needs to be done if those instincts are to be rediscovered. For those misguided souls who still cling to the myth of sexual equality, I address this question: if men and women were intended to carry out similar roles, why — after all the effort and energy which has been devoted to the education of women — are there so few female consultants? Or high court judges? Where be these lady Isambard Kingdom Brunels?

I have written elsewhere of the disasters which would ensue were Project 2000 ever to be implemented, which thankfully it won't. None the less the fallacious principle upon which that scheme was founded is still active in the devious brains of those who would re-create the Nursing Profession on socialist principles.

Who are the people who now extort exorbitant periodic charges for re-admission to my own profession? They are the very same who contest that the secret to all our problems is to raise both entrance standards and salaries to the point where nurses never want to leave the Profession!

But imagine, if you will, a profession where everybody who trained as a nurse actually practised as a nurse. It would be insupportable. Within a month our hospitals would be overflowing with low-calibre registered nurses competing with each other to 'manage' an ever-decreasing band of untrained bedside nurses. Promotion for even the most able would be out of the question and the public coffers would groan under the strain of a spiralling wage bill.

It is quite clear to me that we should once again be building a Nursing Profession which girls want to leave after 18 months. For the majority, nursing should be viewed as a kind of national service, from which they emerge with self-discipline, useful practical experience and a solid offer of marriage.

And if that is the ideal, then our training of the junior nurse must be re-examined. Once we accept the guiding imperative of a fast turnover, rather than a slow one, the necessary changes become obvious. We must increase the emphasis on manual work in the way of cleaning and laundry logistics. While it is desirable that new recruits should be able to read and write, advanced subjects like anatomy and physiology must needs be kept to a minimum.

It is always worth remembering that most patients' knowledge of their inner workings is extremely limited. We have all heard the apocalyptic tale of the invalid who thought his cardiac sphincter was in his stomach. It is a waste of time and resources then to educate those who attend upon the patient in these matters, because they will only confuse the sufferer. There are exceptions of course: when my ward is quiet, I set my girls to learning the correct order of the spinal nerves by rote; this is not because I think the knowledge is inherently valuable, but because the agility of mind produced through such mental exercises is useful in later life, as when compiling Christmas card lists or dinner invitations.

If we were only to return to the traditional values of Nightingale, Project 1860 and the Victorian Golden Age, I could guarantee we would enjoy a superfluity of applicants for training. Applicants who would be prepared to undergo hardship, discipline and modest means in return for the shining reputation and solid start in life which a nursing certificate would afford them.

We *can* create the Nursing Service which our nation deserves. Let us waste no time. The welfare of our patients is at stake!

3 Perennial Preoccupations

Some topics of conversation recur endlessly among nurses. By definition then, these are the subjects which are truly eternal; here is a group of essays dealing with those issues.

It has been argued that religion and history are no longer discussed as regularly or as heatedly as they once were. We include them because they ride high in Miss Plume's philosophical priorities; as far as she is concerned, if they are not widely debated at present, it is time they were. There is probably nobody better equipped than Sister Plume to re-focus them in the public eye.

Men in Nursing

I now wish to treat a subject that has received scant attention, yet deserves much more if we are to truly identify and root out the causes of the decline in this great Profession of ours.

My premonition introduces a subject which should concern us all. To be brief, men in nursing! Does not the very phrase, this palpable contradiction in terms, strike you with its grotesquerie — and cry to heaven itself for correction?

My regular readers will know me as a reasonable woman who chooses the path of moderation in all disputes, sometimes at considerable personal cost. I have sweated and grunted under the arrows of outrageous misfortune, yet the invidious takeover of the Nursing Profession by those of the male sex can no longer be borne.

What has precipitated the deluge of men into the ward, sweeping out traditions long held precious, inveigling themselves into positions of unprecedented power and leading us (albeit 'unwillingly like a snail going to school' as Shakespeare had it) into the realms of Trades Unions and political debate?

In those dear days of my early practice, which we have learnt to call the good old days, men were not even allowed into the Royal College! Now we have a male president, if you please, who speaks on television and in the newspapers as if he actually represents us! Ha! What image of nursing is the nation forming from a man espousing a lot of socialist poppycock? Make no mistake, the public expects the RCN to be represented by an experienced but homely woman of sound common sense whose quiet dedication and stoicism speaks far more eloquently than political rhetoric. What the public does not expect — or want — is men in tweed suits and beards holding forth on John Paul Sartre and Extensionism. Let our vocation speak for us!

The time has come to call a halt, stand up and be counted.

Let us go back to the dawn of time and the humble cave-dwellers of our ancestry. Here the woman would stay at home and raise her children as suited her biological imperative, whilst at the same time caring for the weaker members of the family. Reach for your dictionary and you will find the nurse defined as one who 'gives nourishment and succour, particularly to children'. In Shakespearean times a 'wet nurse' was a young woman of humble origins employed by families of the nobility to care for their infants, washing and toileting them; hence the adjective, 'WET'. (As readers will see, the business of nursing is inextricably interwoven with the duties of child-rearing; that is why nurse training is such an excellent preparation for marriage and motherhood.)

But my analogy does not end here: let us return to our cave and the male of the species; perhaps a slightly rough specimen with few of our social graces, but he knew where his duty lay! While his wife was engaged in the supportive domestic work, he would go out and hunt for food. Fierce, dangerous work, as unsuited to the female as nursing to the male. Readers can well imagine the other chaps' reactions if our Mr Caveman decided that he wanted to stay at home and do the woman's work! Or your reaction, girls, if you had to go out mammoth-hunting! In these days of misplaced liberality we are taught that men doing women's work and vice versa is acceptable. But in those days, man was guided by instinct rather than dogma, and he was happier as a result.

Nowadays of course, we no longer live in caves, but the relationships persist and we alter them at our peril. In our hospitals the female population of nurses maintains a warm safe environment for their charges, whilst the doctors ride out (figuratively speaking) to hunt down disease and — where necessary — to wield the knife! A dramatic metaphor perhaps, but an appropriate one.

Of course one must not make too much of history: to hear most Trades Unionists talk one would think that groups of Tolpuddle martyrs were even now being executed daily on Clapham Common!

How well I remember the first male student nurse on my ward. One would expect a certain diffidence from anybody who was new to the profession, let alone male as well. As it was his brash 'I-know-best' attitude, (a result no doubt of his previous employment as a salesman of some sort) would have brought a state of anarchy to my ward, were it not for some firm management by me.

Within the very first week I had to veto requests to take patients to — of all things — a public house and take steps to prevent the day room being turned into some kind of social club-cum-gambling den. I made it quite clear that if people are well enough to go gallivanting out of the hospital, they shouldn't be there in the first place.

However, not satisfied with stirring the more impressionable patients into near-revolt against routines which took many years of careful planning to establish, he also insisted on addressing the medical staff in terms of easy familiarity which were quite improper. I might add that he was also heard to complain on more than one occasion about having to change in the painter's cupboard, when this had been specially cleared and swept for his individual use. Of all vices, ingratitude of this order must rank among the least becoming to a professional nurse.

The years pass and the system is infested with more and more male nurses. They can be resisted, however, if we do not weaken.

In my writings I follow a long-established precedent of the nurse being viewed as female and the patient as male. I myself am past the stage of constant referrals to textbooks, but one can readily imagine the chaos that would ensue if editors were to re-write their texts with he/she pronoun alternatives merely to satisfy the sexual discrimination lobby.

This conscious act of discrimination — and I am not afraid to term it thus — is not just an aid to editorial convenience, however: it is a witness to the origins of our Profession on the bloody fields of the Crimea where our gallant wounded lads would be buoyed up in their suffering by the seemingly spiritual presence of comely young women ministering to them and reminding them of what they were fighting and dying for. And today: ask a young man in traction upon an orthopaedic ward whether he would prefer a male or female nurse and you can be sure of his reply. Not because of any baser motive, I might add, but purely because women are better equipped to establish a calm healing atmosphere.

I have not the space here to deal fully with the uniform debate, but I **will** say that the attempt to put us into trousers is another folly arising out of the ridiculous drive towards sexual equality, prompted by the presence of males in a female profession. By no means are the sexes equal: each sex has its own qualities and aptitudes which, when properly applied, complement each other to cement the fabric of society.

It is instructive to hear our male nurses complaining of low wages (!) whilst insisting on doing essentially female work. In the final analysis we must question the premise on which the notion of sexual equality in nursing is based. The male nurse is, quite rightly, barred from carrying out certain procedures with female patients where his female counterpart is not so hindered with male patients. This is, as we all know, for the mutual protection of patient and male nurse. But as a ward manager it means that on top of all my other worries and responsibilities I must allocate male nurses to male patients only, or detail a female chaperone to work with him. What a waste of resources! A female student is able to work alone for long periods without intervention from me or other trained nurses. Would that this was true of the male student! A plague upon them, I say, as a symptom of a decadent society and a wart on nursing's body politic!

My advice to male nurses is to take up a profession that more closely follows your instincts, the instincts of the hunter! Leave nursing to those most suited to it!

Uniform

When I began my nursing career, all those years ago, one of the greatest satisfactions for me was donning uniform for the first time. In those days when we put on our uniforms we *felt* somebody, and no grenadier guardsman — nor the Lord Mayor himself — could feel a greater pride than that which rose in our bosoms.

What cared we that our lot was the humble probationer's single stripe? For the world and his wife we were *nurses*, and we had taken our first step on the road that would lead us to the coveted lace cap of the staff nurse, and we could perhaps dream of the day we might don the sacred navy blue of the Sister. (These dreams we quite properly kept to ourselves: ambition has no place in the character of the nurse.)

Now I hear nothing but contempt expressed for our uniform, notwithstanding the increasing liberality of the regulations governing its use. As I have observed before, liberality is the last refuge of the slapdash and oft goes before a fall. I advocate a return to a more sensible uniform and a stricter interpretation of the rules — not merely for reasons of tradition, but hard practicality!

The fact is, people like to see nurses in uniform. Junior doctors enjoy working with nurses who are dressed elegantly; senior doctors need to see at a glance who it is they are dealing with, without having to peer at some illegible name badge. Patients and relatives find it easier to feel — and express — respect when they can identify the traditional symbols of the nurse. And if you have any doubts about the truth of this, you have only to walk on to those misguided psychiatric wards where uniform has been dispensed with: what with patients wearing their outdoor clothes, and nurses in mufti, it's almost impossible to tell patients and nursing staff apart! And then where are you?

Only last week I emerged from my office after a short coffee break with the medical staff to find a staff nurse, with neither cap nor belt, manhandling a patient onto his bed. Suffice to say that under the pretext of an emergency procedure, this girl quite cavalierly removed parts of the uniform to 'make things easier'! I will not countenance such behaviour, and replaced her with a student who thankfully was still properly dressed. What ever next? It will be only a matter of time before nurses are tucking their skirts into their bloomers before lifting patients. Emergency procedures are emergency procedures, but they must never be an excuse for letting our standards drop. It frightens the patients.

No, all civilisations have recognised the value of singling out special groups of individuals by some tangible code of dress and we would do well to recognise the importance of this essentially human tradition, especially as our uniform has such an utilitarian purpose. Even the nurse's cap, that palpable symbol of honourable service, is now under attack, and it will surprise my regular readers not a jot to learn that those self-styled heralds of change, the Americans, have already abolished the cap in many of their hospitals. What fools they be!

Anybody who has the slightest grounding in microbacteriology and germs will know that the cap serves to keep the hair tidy, and prevents the spread of follicle-borne pathogens. And there are so many auxiliary purposes: recognition is one to which I have already alluded, but there are others. Before the totalitarian development of the 'national uniform', (an initiative inflicted upon us by a socialist government and sadly unreversed by the present administration) it was possible to tell at which hospital a nurse had trained, just by the way she folded her cap. Surely, you would think, our lords and masters must recognise that one of the most important elements in the uniform is preventing staff from looking the same? But no: the grace of the London hospital's special headgear has followed the starched apron into obscurity, and we are all the poorer for it.

And further, I ask the political activists of the RCN and GNCC, these holders of ballots and advertisers in newspapers, where was the referendum on the starched apron, and how came you to withdraw it from service without the agreement of the practising nurse? Do you really believe that the modern nurse prefers to sally forth in a pinafore fashioned from polythene? And what of the safety of the patient during bedside procedures? I would like to see the statistical analyses of the number of accidental deaths consequent upon hapless invalids gasping to inhale life-giving oxygen through a plastic apron. And from an economic point of view, where exactly is the cost-effectiveness in disposable aprons which last only 2–3 weeks before falling hopelessly out of shape?

No, as usual, when fashions march, the safety of the patient is the last thing to be considered.

And again: the State Badge, for which I strove for so many years to obtain. Girls complete their training with nothing to show for their efforts, no tangible symbol of their achievement. Yet how impressive nurses used to look when they wore their full regalia: State Registration Badge, School of Nursing Badge, Name Badge, fob watch, scissors chain, pen-clip, pen-torch, spatula and Spencer–Wells forceps. No wonder we enjoyed universal respect when we projected such a readiness for any eventuality.

Our medical colleagues still carry their impedimenta with pride, (our present house officer could carry out minor surgical procedures with the contents of *his* pockets) so why should we relinquish the right to carry the symbols of our office?

Is it not illuminating that our most senior nurses are those with the greatest respect for the uniform and the traditions it bespeaks? Our own Assistant Matron scorned the option of abandoning her uniform and lace cap; unfailingly cool and elegant she is an inspiration to nurse and patient alike. If those who have achieved the highest position in the hospital are keen to wear a proper uniform, it ill behoves the nurse to scorn it. What is good for the Duke of Wellington is good enough for the foot soldier.

If I may speak on a personal note, I greatly resent the changes made to the Sister's uniforms over the years. Fortunately, I had the foresight to hold on to the uniforms I was given in 1963, which although a little faded now and just a little too small for complete comfort, still sport the traditional white piping and lace cuffs of which Florence Nightingale herself would have been proud. I am confident that SHE never meant my younger colleagues to look like till-girls on the six-penny perfume counter at Woolworths!

I am also fortunate to retain some of my St. Thomas's 'frillies', which have worn incredibly well, although too delicate for any but the most special occasions. They are surely a tribute to the workmanship and quality of a past era, and make the modern cap look like used serviettes from a Lyons Tea-shop. My original silver nurse's buckle, a gift from a very dear friend, is also still giving excellent service although, with its clasp no longer functional, I am obliged to secure it by the expedient of two safety pins. Still infinitely preferable to the new-fangled Velcro fastener, which comes undone during exertion with a sound like rending vertebrae. I also prefer to wear a thicker weave of stocking than the regulations specify as protection against the inclemencies of the English climate.

I am proud of my uniform, and it is a pride redoubled whenever a bus conductor says, 'Good Morning, Sister', or I am recognised by a former patient in the grocers.

I always tell my girls something should be done about male nurse's uniforms, i.e. empty them! They always enjoy this little joke. I had not the space to mention the subject in my treatise

on men in nursing, but I can think of no greater evidence of the grotesquerie of the male nurse than their dentist coats and mandarin collars, reminiscent of nothing more than a cross between the faithful servant, Lurch, and the waiters in those awful American restaurants that are so popular. Of course, one never has to look very far for an American influence in the more lunatic reaches of the world of nursing.

My advice is to wear your uniform with pride and, above all, to resist all temptations to venture into trousers!

Religious Services

When one looks at the organisation of the ward, one is struck by the busy atmosphere which prevails; this is not altogether a bad thing because a busy atmosphere means that things are being done, and patients like to feel that things are being done! Not to mention the fact that *I* like to feel that things are being done! We do not employ girls as nurses to stand around chatting: we have perfectly well-qualified Lady Almoners who can do that!

However, I do like to have one period during the day when staff and patients alike can meet, pray together and reflect on the transient nature of human existence. It is an increasingly secular society in which we live, where violence, crime and socialism are on the increase. It is my belief that a greater emphasis on early religious education (with specific reference to the importance of respect for others' property) by teachers and parents alike would prevent much of the vandalism and delinquency that is so rife in our country.

It seems, however, that now — in a period which has seen teachers abandon their professional standing in irresponsible industrial action — others must take up the challenge of the moral and spiritual guidance of the nation; not that people of my generation and experience are ill-equipped for the task; on the contrary, many people look back on the days of my youth with nostalgia as a period of peace and order.

Readers may well profit by hearing how I approach the business of ward-based worship and make my small contribution to the spiritual well-being of Britain.

At 8 o'clock sharp all the patients are sat up in bed and the nurses go through the ward on a bowl round; each patient receives a bowl and a flannel to have a 'freshen-up'. I prefer my patients to stay in bed at this stage as the atmosphere of tranquil contemplation is somewhat marred by men wandering around in pyjamas. On Sundays the padre leads us in our worship, but during the week, as senior member of staff, I deputise for him.

I have the full support of all our visiting clergy, who have provided us with simple orders of service and hymn books. Patients who cannot speak English do, of course, present a problem as they are frequently incapable of following the order of service, but participation in the spirit of the event is still usually possible. Nursing staff can be of great assistance here, demonstrating by sign and gesture when the patient is required to bow his head and close his eyes and so on.

I am extremely fortunate in having amongst my staff an enrolled nurse who, besides being in every way what I would consider a 'good' practical nurse, is also a gifted exponent of the piano-accordion. I like to start with a good rousing hymn; there is nothing quite so stirring to the ailing spirit as a good old-fashioned marching hymn.

With Enrolled Nurse Armstrong leading us, and a junior nurse keeping time on the ward tambourine, we have a really good sing: I jovially call this 'blowing the cobwebs out'. I for one do not believe that religious activity and a little gentle humour are necessarily mutually exclusive! (A managerial note: I always ensure that the privilege of playing the tambourine passes in strict rotation around all my girls; there is no room for favouritism on my ward!)

I am not 'a great preacher of sermons', so I confine proceedings to a short reading from the Authorised Version before addressing a few brief but salient remarks to the assembly. I will, for example, remind the nurses that they are engaged in God's work, or I may direct the patient's attention to the fact that there are many other people in the world who are worse off than they are. Exceptionally, if one patient is particularly ill, I will invite the other patients to mention him in their private contemplations, for which purpose I allocate a short period towards the end of the service. The Lord's Prayer is spoken followed by another good hymn and we are ready to start the day with a common sense of purpose.

Now you may be thinking that on your ward you would not have time to fit such a service into the busy morning routine. But are we not a little too ready to use the excuse of being too busy? If something is important enough we can always make time and I strongly recommend that you do! In fact there is usually plenty of time for breakfast after my little services, and even if an early doctor's round does postpone our morning refreshment, you can always point out to your patients and staff that 'Man does not live by bread alone'.

People are often surprised that my morning services are so successful. The padre himself confided to me that few of the patients expressed any religious interest when he visited them individually. Surely the point lies in the satisfaction of conformity, which — in a herd animal like the human being — is very great. Singing together and reflecting together, we are drawn closer by our common human bond, and share our strengths.

This is why I insist on all the patients taking part. It is the very group participation that is so effective, and I am not going to let that be weakened by a few difficult atheists who are unrepresentative of the population at large. My only general exception to this rule is in the case of patients staying in our private rooms who are allowed — if they wish — to remain in their rooms and commence their breakfasts. As it happens many of these same are the warmest in their appreciation of the ceremony.

Over the years I have encountered few objections from patients or outright refusals to participate. Even amongst those whom I would term 'rough diamonds', there exists a respect for our traditions which soon overrides any tendency towards secularity.

One of my recent patients, a man of some 82 years, and — therefore — more keenly aware than most of the tenuous grip we have on life, enjoyed our services so much that even during acute exacerbations of his distressing condition, which required expeditious transport to the lavatory, his voice could still be heard raised in a spirited rendition of 'Onward Christian Soldiers' culminating in a dignified if muted 'Amen' from his cubicle. I am pleased to say that he has since made a full recovery and insists that he owes his restored health to God and his 'angels in white'.

To conclude, the nurse is in a unique position to improve all aspects of the patient's environment and surely this extends far beyond the limited physical needs of the body. Do not be swayed from your purpose by the red herrings of time or the disinclination of your staff. We are often called upon to do good to people despite themselves and this is surely as true of spiritual ailment as it is of the corporate!

The History of Nursing

Part I

Over the years I have been increasingly concerned about the depth of our young girls' ignorance on the subject of nursing history. If one does not understand how nursing has developed, one cannot hope to defend the principles which underpin the Profession's evolution, and one falls prey to the machinations of socialist commentators, who are only too prepared to rewrite history to suit their prejudices.

I intend therefore to present a précis of the history of the Nursing Profession from earliest times to the present day. Obviously, this broad panorama of human endeavour is beyond the scope of one short essay, so I shall spread my narrative over two sections.

In the fourth century BC, a Greek fellow named Hypocritus developed a code of ethics which is still influential in the modern health service. Even today, young doctors are required to swear the Hypocritical Oath before they can practise: this ensures that only those of the highest moral calibre and integrity are allowed to minister to the public.

Alas, after this brief flaring of the spotlight of progress in the auditorium of medical enterprise, the stage once again fell dark.

In the Christian era, however, the torch was re-lit with the formation of the Order of Deaconesses: these women became the first district nurses and did stalwart service in their local communities.

For many years the Church was to be the focus for healthcare, and during one reorganisation it was decided that, rather than sending the deaconesses out into the community, it was better to bring the sick and needy into one place, so that they might share washing facilities, hassocks and so on. This was not merely an administrative breakthrough. It saved many Deaconesses from the frequent injuries which were the inevitable consequence of propinquity between voluminous habits and swiftly revolving bicycle spokes.

In the twelfth century came the crusades and the foundation of the Order of St. John, an organisation which would probably still be with us today were it not for one major flaw: the nursing was carried out by men!

Although nursing has generally followed a smooth evolutionary path, there have been many occasions on which tactical misjudgements of this sort have set the profession back, sometimes for centuries. History teaches us that men are pathologically unsuited to nursing, but it seems to be a lesson that we must re-learn over and over again.

As for the Monks of St. John, they disappeared into obscurity apart from a few hospitals which they founded in faraway foreign places like Rhodes, Malta and Jerusalem.

No, it was in France in the seventeenth century that the real roots of this great Profession of ours were first revealed. The Augustan Sisters first demonstrated that domestic chores are a vital part of the nursing role, and many of our students would do well to remind themselves of this fact.

It was a difficult time, but they coped with a personal resource and stoicism of which Florence Nightingale herself would have been proud. To save space and limit expenditure on laundry, as many as six patients would share a bed at once. This is an expedient I have suggested myself on numerous occasions, especially on busy admission days, but I have been largely ignored by a blinkered and faint-hearted management.

If there was a fault with the Augustan Sisters, it was perhaps a too stringent insistence on the modesty of their patients. As women of God, their principles forbade them to come within 100 yards of a man without his breeches, and totally ruled out any instruction on basic anatomy or physiology. Although these strictures made practical nursing care a difficult business, they overcame them with ingenious measures which, unfortunately, I have not the space to itemise here.

Some propagandists would have us believe that the Augustan Sisters were actually founded by a man, but we need give this hypothesis no credence. If we are to look for a male protagonist in the history of nursing, then let us salute Good King Hal, Henry VIII, who had the vision to disband the monasteries and insist that the 'Nursing Brothers' took up some occupation more fitting to a man, such as archery. The Battle of Crécy was only just around the corner, and — as in modern times — defence was an important issue.

In the years that followed, the Nursing Profession passed once more into a period of darkness, from which it seemed unlikely to emerge. Instead of insisting on self-discipline and carefully designed hospital routines as the route to the restoration of health, certain busybodies like the Society of Friends maintained that the way to cure ill-health and disease was to throw money at the problem.

Mrs Elizabeth Fry (who should have been at home looking after Mr Fry) often took the public platform to state that if social conditions could be improved, then people would be healthier and happier. Arrant poppycock of course: the poor invariably brought misfortune on themselves by drinking gin, smoking tobacco and refusing to have suitable drains fitted to their dwellings. Despite having credulous friends in high places, the Society of Friends disappeared as quickly as they had come, leaving no lasting impression on the poor or the rich.

The stage was now set for the arrival of Florence Nightingale. The national predicament was dire and the times called for a strong leader; luckily, Fortune delivered one!

Part II

In Part I I described what we may term the pre-history of the Nursing Profession, and now I shall follow the story through the Golden Age of Nightingale and up to the present day.

You will remember that, despite a few well-meaning but ineffectual initiatives, nursing had not developed much in 3000 years: before 1860 there was no national uniform and little discipline.

As is so often the case it takes a good war to accelerate progress, and the war in this case was the Crimean. I have been able to find out almost nothing about the Crimeans, but we do know that they were an honourable people, reluctant to succumb to the jackboot of Russian Bolshevism; our Empire was only too proud to lend a hand in their defence.

At the outbreak of the war, Florence Nightingale was already an experienced nurse. Despite her honourable birth (she was a familiar figure at the Court of Queen Victoria), she had turned her back on luxury to travel the world, observing other people's efforts and formulating her own ideas.

So when the call came from the Duke of Wellington, it was only a matter of days before she had recruited some willing and well-born volunteers, and was ready to board an aeroplane to take her straight to the battle front at Scutari.

The early days were fraught with difficulty: supplies were short and the military surgeons made it clear that they did not approve of women in combat areas. But although Florence faced resistance on every side, she was not to be overcome thus easily. She lost no time in demonstrating her belief in medical supremacy. Once she proved that she and her girls were prepared to carry out the slightest whim of their medical superiors, those who opposed her had to admit defeat and accept the nurses as their subordinates.

This triumph was to set the seal on an unique and powerful relationship which extends to the present day.

It is likely that many of our younger girls — inspired by the nuggets of historical interest that I have spread before them — will be moved to pursue their studies individually into this glorious era. I do not think that too much book-learning is good for the young impressionable mind, but there are several suitable abridged histories on the market that repay further study. Beware, however, of books that offer to slander the memory of those present at Scutari. In my own extensive researches I have come across references to the consumption of alcohol, bullying and discord which, quite obviously, are political propaganda of the very worst kind.

The fact is, Florence Nightingale returned from the Crimea a national heroine. On her return she immediately founded St. Thomas's Hospital. Those nurses who are fortunate enough to work at 'Tommy's' still wear an intensely practical symbol of her achievement in their elegant and ornate headgear.

But time marches on, and even Miss Nightingale's redoubtable powers began to fail. The Profession ran into difficulties almost immediately.

The fight for registration is a problematic area in our history, and it may be that at the time it seemed a good idea. After all, the Register provided something from which to strike malefactors when found guilty of professional misconduct; it offered a sense of achievement to those who gained access to it; and it **used** to qualify one to wear a smart badge.

But recent developments have shown the failings of the system. I do not say that Mrs Bedford-Fenwick could have anticipated that the right of life membership would be rent from the Profession's grasp; I am sure she would have joined me in cursing the day when the GNCC could levy exorbitant fees from me before I could follow my chosen vocation. Suffice to say that Florence Nightingale was a staunch opponent of registration, and that should have been enough for the Profession.

The next major setback came with the establishment of the National Health Service in 1948. Give people anything for nothing and they will cease to appreciate it. The NHS Act opened the floodgates of malingerers who had, until 1948, been held in check by decent Victorian values. Now, any Tom, Dick or Harriet can march into a hospital, demanding free medical and nursing attention, merely on the strength of paying a paltry amount in national insurance contributions.

Where is the justice? I have paid *my* contributions religiously — which as a nurse I can ill afford — yet I have not suffered even one bout of indisposition necessitating admission to hospital. None the less, every day on my ward I am expected to pander to the whims and fancies of people stretched out in luxury on NHS beds.

When the common people fell ill in the past, their symptoms would generally be treated in the home. Possibly with some judicious bleeding or leeching, or if all else failed, rubbing a dock leaf on the affected part. With the benefit of hindsight we know these treatments to have been wholly ineffective, but they gave psychological comfort. And, even if most people did die of their maladies in those days, at least they did it on their own resources, without expecting a nanny state to do all their suffering for them.

It will not surprise the attentive reader that I view the recent history of this nation, and the Nursing Profession in particular, with considerable disquiet. I see a once-proud nation cowed by the onward march of socialism and liberalism. I see a Nursing Profession losing its grip on the traditions and disciplines which made it great.

All is not gloom, however. I also see glimmers of hope winking on the horizon that bespeak a rebirth of all that nurses of my generation hold dear. If I am pressed to quote positive omens for the future I would cite triumphs such as the collapse of the Nursing Process; the new suspicion of intellectualism and all things American; the reintroduction of the Matron as an important figure in our hospitals — a mantle I might have been prepared to adopt myself, were I not wedded to the bedside role.

History shows us what women of resilient character and indomitable virtue may achieve if they hold firm to their principles. But beware! The forces of evil are baying at our portals and we must prepare for the storm ahead!

Research

Speaking as an essentially practical nurse, I find the endless discussions about nursing research impossible to bear in silence. Now research is a very good thing in its place; there can be few of us alive today who have not benefited from the vision and determination of the great men of medical science: where would we be without Lister's antiseptics, Simpson's anaesthesiae, or Andrews' Liver Salts?

But research is emphatically and undeniably the rightful domain of the doctor, as the sluice is the appropriate area for the student nurse. Those who argue for nursing research are the same quasi-intellectuals who seek to turn this great Profession of ours into a mere technical specialism. You will hear them claiming to be establishing an independent body of knowledge unique to nursing; this is arrant enough poppycock on its own, but it conceals a far more sinister purpose. Their real aim is to make the simple Art of Nursing incomprehensible to its own most experienced practitioners; these revolutionaries are confident that under the confusion spread by their talk of 'models' and 'variables', they will be able to wrest control of the Profession away from its rightful inheritors.

Such is the insidious growth in the research faction that we can no longer open the *Nursing Times* without coming across some impenetrable treatise devoted to abstract and totally irrelevant topics, peppered with American jargon and complex diagrams. Fortunately, most nurses are far too sensible to waste their time wading through all this rubbish. They instinctively mistrust research because it so often seeks to undercut and discredit methods which have been accepted for over a century.

Only last month I had the misfortune to have a 'Research Nurse' billeted on me. I consider this an unforgivable invasion of privacy. This woman, who has scarce been qualified for 3 years (I made it my business to determine this at an early stage), claimed to be investigating the efficiency and management approach of my ward. This apparently entailed trailing around after me, asking a lot of fool questions. If she had really been interested in ward efficiency, she could have rolled her sleeves up and got stuck into a few bedbaths, but of course, if she was interested in real nursing, she would never have signed up with the research brigade in the first place.

Frankly, if she had been one of my staff nurses, she wouldn't have lasted very long. No activity seemed safe from her busybodying. I might be carrying out a drug round, and suddenly she would appear behind me like an unquiet spirit, asking things like 'Why is Mr Reynolds still on steroids?' Now, as every good nurse knows, patients' analgesia is a matter for the doctors. I am here to dispense medications in line with their instructions; I can hardly be expected to know all the whys and wherefores of intricate treatments, which change from day to day anyhow. Needless to say, I sent her away with a flea in her ear, and she left me to carry out my drug round in peace.

Worse was to come, however. Having failed in her attempts to intimidate me with her interrogation, she turned her attention to the learner nurses. I discovered her attempting to hold subversive meetings with my students in the clinical room.

When I intervened she was already passing out 'reading materials' which advanced the heresy that pressure area care may be undertaken without recourse to oxygen or egg white. All the good work I had done with my young girls, long hours spent on back-round practice and correcting misconceptions they had picked up in the School of Nursing, was undone in a minute. These impressionable young nurses needed much reassurance and coercion before they would return to my tried and trusted methods.

But as I closed one avenue for trouble making, so she would open up on another front. Her next target was the very patient, lying ill in bed. Returning from some midweek leave, I discovered that she had circulated a series of questionnaires among the sick, which invited them to comment on various aspects of their care and treatment, and award marks from one to five. Needless to say, the mob of malcontents and malingerers who currently infest my ward enjoyed making impertinent criticisms: they did not even have the common decency to confine themselves to the grading system, but appended further offensive remarks in the margin. Obviously those who are ill can hardly be expected to advance objective opinions. I want to know when I will be given a questionnaire to complete, detailing the frailties of my patients!

Fortunately I was able to contain these attacks on my integrity, and Mrs Know-it-all was soon on her way to some other unfortunate ward.

The march of progress as personified by those occupied in research must be resisted at all costs. For those of us who do take a pride in tradition, there are some comforting aspects to the research question. With all the research work undertaken, all the forests sacrificed to produce questionnaires, all the hot air expended in fatuous specialist symposia, instinctive, basic nursing practice has not changed one iota. We are made of sterner stuff.

Most research work finally comes to rest in obscure intellectual journals which moulder away in the hidden corners of dusty libraries. As we go on the offensive against research frauds, let us demand a true assessment of their supposed contribution. Let us be told what they have achieved. And when it is admitted that the sum total is negligible, let us demand that the funding of their harebrained timewasting is stopped forthwith.

Hypocritus and Galen never needed grants from the Universities or Health Authorities to continue their researches; they pursued **their** art because they were committed to the furtherance of useful human knowledge and the well-being of their fellow man. Let us see how many research nurses are prepared to go hungry in pursuance of *their* studies.

When I leave my ward after a day's labour, 28 patients are the better for it. If the thousands of nonsensical research programmes were cancelled, we could afford to pay for more real nurses like me, who care for real patients. The time has come to flush out the parasites; the welfare of our patients is at stake!

4 Colleagues and Charlatans

Nurses do not work in isolation, but as important members of a complex and multidisciplinary team. Over the years, that team has widened steadily to embrace new skills, technologies and methodologies; with a nation at once more health-conscious and apt to look beyond the limits of orthodox medicine, there is a danger that health care will become both confused and confusing.

Here Sister Plume assesses the relative importance of certain key groups of health-care professionals with her usual perspicacity and objectivity.

Medical Staff

Who — according to the trendy faddists and rabid left wing — is responsible for the parlous state of today's health service? The Trades Unions? The legions of parasites huddled round the doors of our Casualty department trying to gain illicit access to staff supplies of coffee and tea? Socialist politicians who have artificially elevated the expectations of the masses to such a height that no increase in the provision of the welfare state could ever satisfy them? These would be reasonable suggestions, and ones with which I would sympathise.

But no! If you are a follower of Karl and Engels — the Marx brothers — you would look in quite a different direction for *your* target. If your self-avowed purpose is to dismantle the establishment, you must seek out the most honoured and respected members of the community and sully their characters. This, it seems to me, is what lies behind the current fashion for criticising our medical colleagues, the doctors.

To hear some individuals holding forth on the so-called failings of our physicians and surgeons, one would think they were the scourge and direst enemies of the health service, rather than the central pool of talent and bedrock on which it depends.

I cannot speak of the general practitioners. Thankfully I have had little reason to visit my local surgery over the years: a robust constitution has been my reward for a loyal commitment to the service of others. As we all know, illness more easily strikes those to whom honest labour is a stranger. Consequently I know my own GP only socially. But even he, whose preoccupations will always lie in the more mundane areas of the healer's art — the head cold, the bunion, the bad nerves — even this humble GP I say, has selflessly sacrificed his youth and enjoyments in the pursuit of that knowledge which is our support and staff in times of adversity.

How much heavier a responsibility then, is that of the hospital doctors, and how much greater should be our debt of gratitude to these truest hiers of Hypocritus, who confront and vanquish the mortal ills of a nation sick in spirit as in health.

It may surprise some of my readers (perhaps less familiar with medical history than those of us who have lived and served through all the most crucial stages of hospital history) that the doctors for whom they so gladly labour do not even enjoy the benefit of employee status, as we do. How selfless are these men, who put their professional duty before any thought of financial gain, sneering at wealth and investing their prime in those other members of society to whom the sacred grasp of poverty is no stranger.

On my ward, I am blessed with a wonderful team, from the authoritative figure of our consultant down to the boyish vigour of our young house officer, taking his first steps on the path of an honourable career. Our consultant, Mr Brown, is not without his idiosyncrasies, but I feel he is entitled to them. His wisdom is our mainstay and his peccadilloes are a palpable proof of his deep humanity.

Sometimes I have had to counter complaints about his abrupt manner in dealing with patients, and particularly his custom of addressing them by their surnames. Let me say this: at least he knows his patients well enough to get their names right most of the time, with only a little prompting from me or the house officer!

We must appreciate that to the surgeon of genius each pathological condition takes on a character of its own, with which he has done battle repeatedly over the years. We may see Mr Arnold in bed and know how much he smokes, where he works and what condition his bedsores are in, but for the professional surgeon, Mr Arnold is merely another manifestation of his old enemy, the appendix. People vary from each other in a most troublesome way, but one case of appendicitis is very much like another.

It must be said that in many of the battles between doctor and disease, the patient seems to fraternise with the enemy! One sees patients persisting in unhealthy practices such as the drinking of alcohol, the smoking of tobacco or displaying an unsavoury interest in the nature of their disease and treatment. If one is to deliver oneself into the care of Mr Brown, and I can think of none better to deliver oneself unto, it simply does not do to be continually cross-examining him on 'how things are going'. The surgeon is doing his best, and the patient must be content that — if it is destined to be — he will recover. If not, any amount of impertinent enquiry will scarcely save his life.

Medical staff nowadays face a greater-than-ever barrage of queries and challenges, and I for one can excuse a certain peremptoriness in their manner, especially when one considers that most illness is self-inflicted anyway.

I do not say that consultant surgeons are always omniscient; far from it. To err is human, and surgeons **are** human, albeit of a very superior type. For the last 10 years of Mr Brent's rule, for example, we all knew that his judgement had deteriorated somewhat. Although an extremely well-preserved 70, the stresses and strains of his professional life took their toll, and this once great surgeon was increasingly wont to seek solace in alcoholic liquors.

This was the surgeon whose proudest boast was that he had once amputated his batman's leg on the field of battle in less than 10 minutes without anaesthetic, thus saving his trusty servant from the inconvenience of the long journey back to the field hospital and separation from his master. Indeed it was this experience that first led Mr Brent to consider a career in medicine following his discharge from the Army.

But the ravages of age and pink gin produced an unhappy contrariness of nature in this once-great surgeon, which found unnerving expression in a flat contradiction of any course of action ordered by his juniors.

The senior registrar and I became aware that patients were, perhaps, ill-served by the constant changes and reversals in therapy occasioned by such a circumstance, and were forced to hit upon a simple yet bold expedient by which all patients might thrive.

After due consideration, and with my agreement, my registrars would suggest courses of action in opposition to the one which their judgement would have naturally led them. If a drainage tube needed to stay in for a longer period post-operatively, we would say, 'We had thought, Sir, of removing the drain **today**, Sir.' Invariably Mr Brent would retort, 'Be d----d man, what are you playing at, it needs to stay in for another 5 days at least.' This same was accompanied by oaths and imprecations disturbing in their ferocity, but none the less the right strategy was finally decided upon and the status quo preserved.

The wonderful thing about the medical hierarchy is that there are safeguards built into the system. We have all suffered the occasional inefficient or even dangerous practitioner but, by and large, the consequences of mistakes are minimised by the solidarity and loyalty of the rest of the team.

It ill behoves nursing staff or anyone else to criticise a system which offers such security. Stand by your doctors and defend them from obliquity; they deserve it!

Alternative Therapies

If I were to recommend that my readers should insert plugs of dried plantain leaf into their ears as a protection against influenza, I can imagine that there would be some reluctance to comply, even amongst my most loyal and ingenuous followers. But surely this proposition is no more nonsensical than any of the counsel offered by the mobs of so-called 'alternative therapists', currently laying siege to our health-care system.

It is obvious to me that these alternative therapies — whether emanating from homeopaths, osteopaths, psychopaths, herbalists, astrologers or necromancers — are all part of an orchestrated strategy to wrest influence and esteem from the medical establishment. It is some very few months since I last took up cudgels on behalf of our medical colleagues; they are a group of men who have traditionally enjoyed universal approbation, but now face obliquity and criticism from sinister and insidious sources.

It is easy to repulse the full-frontal ideological attacks of radical intellectuals: one has only to consider and quote the great achievements of physicians through the ages, Hypocritus, Kildare and Fleming, to be convinced of the infallibility of the Profession. These men made great sacrifices to develop and refine techniques and apparatus to prolong useful lives, and their modern counterparts carry the same torch just as deciduously.

But the alternative therapists do not argue openly or accept defeat in an honest, straightforward way: this is why they are so dangerous. Instead they choose to exist on the fringes of the National Health Service, parasites on the achievements of orthodox medicine.

Of course, charlatans can not, and do not, offer any genuine alternative: if **you** were to undergo surgery, would you prefer to be attended by a highly-trained and professional anaesthetist, or a wild-eyed woman brandishing acupuncture spikes? No doubt sticking needles into people had its place in the punitive system of the Tang Dynasty, but it is hardly something one can put one's faith in when facing a highly-selective vagotomy!

It must be obvious to all who work in hospital service that health is the product of a wholesome lifestyle supported by the occasional intervention of a properly qualified medical practitioner. The health cranks, with their muesli and herbal tablets, are not concerned with prolonging life or educating people against abuse of their bodies.

It will not have escaped the attention of my more perspicacious readers that those who seek solace in herbalism and

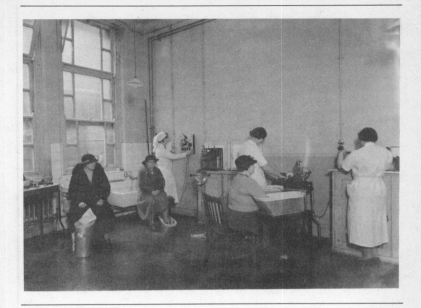

quackery today are the very same generation who abandoned
themselves to mind-expanding drugs and sexual licentiousness
in the nineteen-sixties. Having failed to convince us that
'flower power' was the answer to the world's ills, they now
reappear in a different guise, advocating that we should wash
our hair in goats' urine or give birth in a swimming pool. (This
latter stroke of genius was a typically French innovation, but
none the less it incensed me enough to tear up my season-ticket
for the municipal baths.)

You may say that these people do no harm with their patent
medicines and crack-brained schemes. One has heard stories of
people who have been admitted through the casualty department with overdoses of medications such as 'essence of Haw-
thorn'. Having referred to the relevant experts it transpires that
to have any significant effect the victim would need to ingest
some 75,000 of these pills, and even then experience only a tiny
headache and a mild sweat. If we were to scold the patient with
the remonstrance 'it never achieves anything does it?', we
would be speaking the truth in more ways than one. But
because their remedies are largely ineffective, this is no reason

to doubt that the practitioners themselves are inimical to everything we hold dear.

In past eras, when the British people had a firmer grasp on the moral imperatives of life, charlatans and the hawkers of patent medicines would be burnt at the stake, or — if the populace were feeling particularly genial — tarred and feathered. But liberality and its associated squeamishness have robbed us of any truly effective way of dealing with these rogues. No longer do they have to trail from village to village, spurned as the vagrants that they are; now brass plates, interviews with the more hysterical media and riches beyond the dreams of most ordinary physicians are their lot. They are successfully inveigling themselves into the establishment.

Did you know, for example, that hypnosis was freely available on the National Health Service? In my youth I attended a theatrical performance in which the great Angus McClean (an Italian illusionist) demonstrated his skills. There is no doubt that in convincing susceptible and impressionable individuals that they were planks of wood, or fields of buttercups, he was immensely successful. None the less, one would hardly wish to entrust one's hip replacement to such an illusionist, no matter how impressive his technique. I know that even the most co-operative of my patients expects more in the way of pre-operative preparation than having a student nurse wave a fob watch over him.

Only last week, at the insistence of dubious elements within the 'In-service training department', my own hospital's bolshevik cell, I attended a magic lantern slide show dedicated to the subject of therapeutic touch. No warnings were given to me or any of my girls prior to the show, which consisted of colour photographs depicting patients in varying degrees of mystical transport. This state was induced — so we were invited to believe by our gushing narrator — through the 'laying on of hands'.

This is exactly the kind of unchristian behaviour that one expects to see creeping in to ward practice when nursing educationists indulge their modernist whims. The individuals inflicting their 'therapeutic touch' on victims were also everything you might expect. Long-haired, bearded, dissolute-looking youths, whose expressions suggested that they might — at the slightest provocation — begin speaking in tongues.

On being asked to act as a subject for a practical demonstration of this art, I summoned my girls about me, and was back on the ward in time for the 3 o'clock back round.

Osteopaths are another case in point, and I speak from knowledge. Their current veneer of respectability should not fool readers who are aware of the unspeakable deeds that are sanctioned by this group of latter-day torturers. A distant relative of mine was once treated by an Osteopath; treated in a way I might add that under any normal circumstances would have invited criminal proceedings under the laws of assault and battery. It gives some measure of the impact of the various twisting and pummelling attacks on my relative that he was led to claim that he felt much improved after his treatment. He did not deceive me: it was obviously a subterfuge by which he hoped to prevent the ogre who had attended him from returning and starting all over again.

The truth must be faced. Anybody can set up shop as an alternative therapist, without so much as a brass plate by way of capital. Contrast this with the ease of mind associated with a visit to a properly qualified medical practitioner. One knows that there are always doctors available who represent the finest tradition of English gentlemen. They generally went to good schools, and one of the better universities; if their people are not actually in the medical field, they will have been in some equally respectable profession; they will have a strong sense of tradition, and a respect for the proprieties of doctor–nurse–patient relationships; above all they will not recommend that you bind your cuts in muslin and horse-dung poultices.

Let us align ourselves with the powers of medical orthodoxy, and ensure that no support or encouragement is given to the motley crew of cranks, quacks and lunatics!

Meal-times

If Man does not, in truth, live by bread alone, the message seems to have been lost on the editorial staff of the *Nursing Times* and all the other hysterical nutritional faddists in our midst. One should expect symptoms of impaired judgement from those who survive on a diet of kidney beans and cucumber bakes, but my patience is wearing thin with the apparently endless Care about Food campaign. A little joke I have with my girls is that while my patience is *wearing* thin, my patients are *growing* thin! You may laugh, just as my girls do, but this is a humorous way of making a very serious point: have we forgotten that it is patients we are supposed to care for, not menu plans?

No, the sign of the shiftless, rebellious individual has always been the mindless questioning of tried and trusted methods, and we must accept that it was only a matter of time before the fickle attentions of the liberals and communists were turned on the traditional diet of these islands. But if the British diet is really so unwholesome, why is my ward full of persons who have reached advanced years whilst eating all the foods so roundly condemned by the self-styled experts?

Of course, if there were any consistency in the advice that is heaped upon us by these people, we might be prepared to pay more attention to their exhortations. But the fact is, while one eminent physician is telling us to cut down on fats, another is telling us that the secret of eternal life is fibre, or **fiber** as guess-which-nation calls it. Only a few weeks ago another worthy was stating that he had lived happily and healthily for 60 years on a diet consisting entirely of potato crisps. The conclusion that I draw from all this debate is that it must be much easier to become a doctor in America than it is in England.

It is obvious to me that planning meals for patients is largely a matter of instinct and common sense. When I was young we never knew anything about calories or roughage, but we thrived on good plain food, and were a jolly sight healthier than today's youth for all their fast health foods and courgettes.

Unfortunately I have not the space here to enter into a lengthy dissertation on meal provision in the ward area, but I will offer up some pointers which my less experienced colleagues may find helpful.

Firstly let me say that the invalid must not be overfaced with huge portions. Let us not use two potatoes where one may suffice; like the artist who knows how to use areas of blank canvas to dramatic effect, so must we realise that restraint is important in making food attractive, and we do not need to cover the whole plate by any means. Now that we are finally becoming a little more cost-conscious, it must be clear to all but the most intractable socialists that it is not economic to provide endless supplies of victuals for persons who make up the unproductive part of society; this is even more crucial when one considers the inflated prices we are obliged to pay for foodstuffs sold by the iniquitous and avaricious farmers of Europe.

Most of our patients nowadays are elderly, and their dentition often leaves much to be desired. It is not uncommon in my experience to find that these patients have barely finished their soup course before it is time to remove the meal tray, so that main course and sweet are completely wasted. But readers will know that I am not slow to embrace progress where it can be proved of tangible benefit to the patient. Thank goodness for the electric liquidiser! Now for patients over 60 or without the blessing of their own teeth, we can swiftly reduce all the elements of the meal into one easily digested, semi-solution; thus meal-times cease to offer the irksome interruption to routine they did in the past.

The densest introductory course nurse knows that sick people have poor appetites anyway. As far as I am concerned, a patient who demands large meals and second helpings is not — by definition — sick, and should not be occupying bed space in a National Health Service hospital. If it's a hotel they want, they should have made some provision for private care. Of course, a returning appetite is a good sign and cause for celebration, as long as it is followed swiftly by plans for discharge.

Having limited meals to sensible proportions, the next step is to ensure that relatives are persuaded not to bring foodstuffs onto the ward. Nurses have the primary responsibility for monitoring nutritional intake; effective control cannot be maintained if the perfectly adequate diet supplied is supplemented by outside sources. Let me say that there would be far less food wasted and fewer complaints if patients were required to pay for their own food whilst in hospital, as the nursing staff are. (I might add that the poor quality and sparseness of the meals offered in the staff canteen is little short of a scandal. How I mourn the passing of the elegance and comfort of the Sisters' Dining Room!)

Those people who complain about hospital food should have been around in the days of my youth, when whole families lived entirely on boiled carrots and rice pudding, and rickets and malnutrition were commonplace!

Nurses must be constantly vigilant for attempts at exoticism in menus. We have all been bombarded with information about food additives and their potentially harmful effects. Yet the powers that be insist on producing fancy foreign dishes for staff and patients alike. How are we to identify the flavourings and colourings that poison our food when we can't even see what we're eating? Yes, it's easy enough to ridicule good plain English food, like sausages, macaroni cheese or plum duff, but at least you can't hide any of these modern chemicals in them!

I blame the dietitians. Catapulted from the role of cooks to that of clinical adviser, they now expect to participate in ward rounds and even go round talking to patients if you please! I don't mind involving the odd physiotherapist in a round as long as they don't make too much noise and are attentive to the doctors. I **do** object to having American-style catering staff bursting in upon our deliberations just because they know how to make egg flip without getting yolk on the ceiling.

Their only redeeming feature as far as I am concerned is that none of their lunatic interventions ever seem to make the slightest difference to the food that actually arrives on the ward. They may fill out 57,000 of their pink forms a year, but Mr Singh still gets his sausages and plum duff: this is a victory for common sense.

So my advice is to resist the forces of faddism that are intent on destroying traditional customs and tastes. After all, when has a vegetarian ever won a gold medal at the Olympic Games, or become Prime Minister? You can be sure that our empire was not built by people who ate cauliflower cheese and sunflower seed biscuits! Let us rally to the call of 'Plain Food for Plain People'!

Agency Nurses

As the long day's duties draw to a close and I look forward to the few hours' leisure that fall to my lot, it has been my habit to reflect on the pleasures to come. Will I settle down with some devotional volume or tune in to a favourite wireless programme? Should I seclude myself with a warming cup of cocoa, or abandon myself to the sensual delight of a glass of herb tea and a plate of Lincoln biscuits? With such pleasing ruminations have I been wont to employ the closing minutes of the evening shift, secure in the knowledge that enjoyments hard-earned are enjoyments doubly welcome!

But recent developments have shattered the tranquillity and decorum of what Shakespeare elegantly expressed as the 'posteriors of the day'. No longer can I go to my rest with that ease of mind which blesses the conscientious. Instead I must lie awake at night, a tumult in my brain and a cold sweat upon my brow as a thousand potential disasters pass before my mind's eye. The reason? The management of my hospital have decided — in their limited wisdom — to employ nurses from a commercial agency to work the night shift.

Let me say at the outset that I have been seldom content with the level of cover my ward receives at night. The decline in standards amongst students, and the youth of the Night Sisters, is enough to give any senior nurse pause for troubled thought.

None the less, in the past I have been consoled by the fact that nothing very much ever happens at night and that our nocturnal staff are cast very much in the role of caretakers until the hour of the morning when proper routines can be reinstated.

As long as they don't interfere with any of my apparatus, or leave the ward untidy, then I have been satisfied. Needless to say I always insist that disposable paper sheets are used at night because I cannot allow the depletion of valuable linen stocks which are required for the morning bed-making round.

I also ensure that other vital resources such as tea, coffee and the doctors' biscuits are secured under lock and key. The hours of darkness are those which Providence has set aside for the repose of the invalid. It serves nobody's purpose to serve stimulating beverages between supper and breakfast time.

Amongst my regular night staff I have obtained a commitment to silence after lights out. When I look at the Nursing Records in the morning I expect to see 28 identical entries of 'Good night, slept well'. Night nurses who write anything else are clearly failing in their duty — and I automatically report them to their superiors.

But these strictures apart, I have maintained a state of uneasy truce with the night staff over the years which has survived all attempts at interference from the radical troublemakers such as the Nursing Process Co-ordinators and clinical teachers who have been relegated to the night shift.

Times have changed. In recent weeks, on repeated occasions, I have come to give my night report and found nurses in strange American-style uniforms wearing — and I warn my more sensitive colleagues to prepare themselves for a shock — **cardigans**! I am well aware that our heating system leaves much to be desired, but if the patients can survive the inclemencies of the environment, then I am sure the nurses can endure the occasional seasonal icing.

Worse than their jarring dress-sense, however, is the fact that they are totally unknown to me. In a tight-knit hospital community such as ours, one makes it one's business to find out nurses' backgrounds, who their people are and whether they have any private means. This is common-sense management. For all I knew these women might have been central co-ordinators for the Revolutionary Trotskyist Party; on telephoning Nursing Administration, I was told that these were in fact from the Friend-in-Need private agency who had come to 'help out'.

Having interrogated them sufficiently I found this indeed to be the case. As I had no alternative but to agree their presence — apparently there was not so much as an introductory course nurse available throughout the hospital — I gave way. To my eternal regret. Once having agreed to this imposition, I became a target for these profiteers in their Crimplene and cosmetics: I certainly cannot imagine that other wards are ill-used to the same degree.

Fortunately I have been able to take certain steps designed to minimise the risks of outright catastrophe.

I will suffer no nurse to work on my ward unless she first presents her credentials and certificates of qualification for my approval. I then set a few questions on general nursing subjects to ensure that the individual to whom I entrust my ward has at least some basic grasp of the rudiments. I am proud to say that no nurse has ever worked on my ward who could not recite from memory the year of Florence Nightingale's birth or the colour of the State Midwife's uniform in 1942.

When the agency nurses first started coming, very few passed the tests, but now there are many more first-time successes. Some even seem quite keen to take part, rushing straight from the Nursing Administration block to my ward as if they were afraid of forgetting something. But if their general nursing knowledge is improving, then their moral tone certainly is not.

This should not surprise us: nurses who work for private agencies are selling their birthright for a mess of porridge. Seduced by the allure of astronomical wages, they have turned their backs on the hardship and self-denial which are an inherent part of the nursing heritage.

This was made graphically clear when I confronted one agency nurse with her avarice. She told me that she wished to be married and that she feared that she and her intended would be unable to purchase a dwelling without some additional income.

On asking her why she did not seek some honourable and regular employment in a hospital, she replied that she already had an appointment in a neighbouring hospital. I was deeply shocked.

I had long suspected that greed and lack of principle were prevalent in some areas of our Profession, but never did I expect to meet such a brazen example.

Before dismissing her from the ward I gave her a brief but telling sermon on the subject of self-denial and the duties of a husband. He it was who should be providing for their wants; if she had a solid offer of marriage, she should be using her leisure hours to ingratiate herself with her new relations and knitting items for her bottom drawer. And if finance was scarce then she must needs postpone the day of her nuptials: my mother was engaged to my father for no less than 15 years before she could tie the knot and it certainly never did her any harm. I am sure my father was of the same opinion.

She — the agency nurse — departed a chastened and wiser individual, and I was gratified to hear from our Assistant

Matron that she had expressed — with great warmth — her reluctance to work at our hospital ever again, so I imagine my words must have had some beneficial effect.

And I must exhort all my colleagues to cleave just as indefatigably to your principles. The rise of the Agency Nurse is just one more step on the slippery slope to ruin for this great Profession of ours. Challenge them, question them and refuse them access wherever possible. They shall not pass!

Privatisation

One of the subjects which the *Nursing Times* has contemporaneously refused to address, is the issue of non-medical staff and their (low) position in the hospital hierarchy.

In these days of socialism and I'm-all-right-Jack radicals, it is easy to forget that one of the prime objectives of the hospital is to be cost-effective. It is inevitable that monies must be diverted from the central coffers to care for the sick and needy, but we must be sure that this amounts to no more than is absolutely necessary.

And of the fiscal component, we should be diverting the lion's share to those people who have devoted their lives to the Profession, such as Ward Sisters.

This is why I welcomed the arrival of contract staff at St. Hilda's to take over functions such as cleaning, laundry and catering. Now do not mistake my purpose: these three functions are really the domain of the junior nurse. (I have campaigned long and hard for my girls to be allowed to take over ward cleaning; so far, unfortunately, with little support.)

But a misguided quest for specialism robbed us of these satisfying areas of responsibility, and instead transferred them to the so-called hotel services. Most appropriate, as the people 'employed' in this area have used St. Hilda's as if it were a five-star hotel with themselves as the guests.

Everybody knows that porters and domestic staff are exorbitantly overpaid, and that is simply because they are militantly unionised and can hold the country to ransom whenever they feel the need to buy a third car or extend their *en suite* swimming pool. In the meantime, those of us who are moral objectors to industrial action must work long hours for a mere pittance, just as if we were student nurses rather than highly qualified professionals. I have never been afraid of hard work, and I advocate it for my girls on every occasion; but nowadays my skills and talents are better employed in a supervisory and co-ordinating role.

However, with the arrival of contract staff, things seem set for a positive change. The fresh air of healthy competition is already blowing through the fetid passages of the liberal-ridden NHS, and we can again look for a domestic service who are rewarded as befits their station (and no better), proper discipline, and higher standards all round.

During the early days of privatisation there were, of course, some teething problems, as one might expect from any truly great enterprise. And with a ghastly inevitability, the troublemakers and malcontents crawled out of the woodwork to begin their carping about 'standards' and 'exploitation'. We may expect resistance from those for whom progress is erythema; the Trades Unions have a vested interest in keeping things as they are, for they are riding the same gravy train as the fat-bellied administrators and managerial theoreticians. But speaking as one who embraces change wherever it can be demonstrated to be beneficial to the hospital service, I say 'Forward!', and down with the detractors.

The fact is, ward cleaning is now accomplished by a smaller staff, and on the occasions when the state of the ward does fall below the pristine, my girls are ideally positioned to bring things up to scratch with some good honest elbow grease. Not only are we spending less money on cleaning, but for the first time in a decade, junior nurses have the opportunity to learn the real nuts and bolts of their craft.

I am supported in this view by Mr Jerry Vulpine, who is the Chief Executive (Europe) of the Universal Cleansing Institute, the organisation whose services have been retained by St. Hilda's. He has been a regular visitor to my ward, perhaps sensing in me a kindred spirit. And scarcely such a visit goes by without he offers us some tokens of his esteem, such as a bunch of daffodils or items of confectionery for my girls.

It was at his suggestion that I have used the ward fund to purchase equity in his company, as well as making some modest investments of my own. As Mr Vulpine has pointed out, we are now very much a share-owning society, and it is to the infinite benefit of our patients if the staff have a tangible and profitable stake in the company that provides such vital services to our hospital. And for once my views are in sympathy with our management, many of whom have also seen the benefits of placing the business relationship on a more mutually profitable basis.

Now, for the first time, the hospital system is generating wealth rather than merely dissipating it, and those involved in the provision of care have discovered a new motivation.

Another major step forward has been the contracting out of surgical operations to private hospitals. The plain fact of the matter is that since we were forced to close two of our operating theatres we have not been able to meet demand; but this has had certain associated benefits for many of our professional colleagues.

Our Orthopaedic Surgeon used to spend an inordinate amount of time travelling by motor car from St. Hilda's to the Mansion Private Hospital, where he also had many professional commitments. As he has argued, if he could spend all his time at the Mansion, resources now allocated to the maintenance of two separate operating theatres — not to mention transport costs — could be focused back where they would do most good. He has also pointed out the incalculable benefits to the environment, because he will no longer be polluting the atmosphere with the noxious emissions from his conveyance as he makes his way between the hospitals. So why aren't Greenpiece campaigning on behalf of public-spirited individuals like this surgeon? The answer is simple: they are green with envy, not benevolence!

It is clear to me that if we are ever to return to the golden age of English Nursing, we must stop living in the past, and fearlessly embrace the challenges of the commercial arena!

Letter to a Sister

It is not my custom to answer letters personally as I believe the material in my articles covers everything any young girl needs to know about nursing. My readers will appreciate that I receive so many messages of support from around the country — and even the colonies on occasion — that I scarcely have time to address personal preoccupations.

But I have recently received a letter from a young girl which demands that I make an exception. The communication came from a person of no more than 26 years who has had the misfortune to be appointed as a Ward Sister. She called out to me in her torment for counsel. Apparently her junior staff, particularly the nursing auxiliaries, were expressing vocal concern at the youth of their 'leader', and had enlarged upon their concerns with a more general complaint that modern Sisters seem to have 'lost their grip'.

We may well be sympathetic to a young girl who has had the mantle of seniority thrust upon her before she has sufficient experience to carry it convincingly. But how much more sorry must we be for her unfortunate junior colleagues who are saddled with the liability of youth. One can well imagine the frustration and outrage they suffered when they realise that routines they have carefully established over many years — that treatments which have proven to stand the test of time — are likely to be swept away in the face of a misguided agent of progress.

I do not know for certain that the girl involved is actually one of the revolutionaries who threaten to dismantle the profession. But her letter did contain references to suspicious practices such as 'treating the patient as an individual'.

But if her only fault is youth, that must be enough. Twenty-six is a ludicrous age to become a Sister; it took me 30 years before I reached my first Sister's post, and even then there was some opposition to my appointment. One of my very dear friends — Deidre Manners — would never have achieved her Sister's post at all if she had not persuaded her father to purchase a new wing for the maternity department!

For too long our nation has been in the thrall of the Cult of Youth. We have been persuaded that all virtues reside with the young, although a close examination of the facts easily exposes the fallacy: most crime is committed by the young; most revolutionaries and socialists are young; the young rush about, play pop music and generally use up more than their fair share of space and resources. In our own Profession the lamentable decline is most marked among the young — the students. It is they who — under the influence of a few agent provocativists — have thrown over the bulwarks and lodestones of tradition.

In my day, there were no such things as teenagers. One progressed straight from childhood to adulthood at the age of 21, or 12 if one belonged to the lower orders.

If we are to identify the real reasons behind the fact that modern Sisters are 'losing their grip' we must adopt a historical perspective. When I entered the Profession I embarked upon a long and arduous professional quest which would **eventually** lead me to the coveted lace of the Sister. But I had to make certain choices. I could either set my sights on promotion, or I could marry and propagate. I could not do both.

Because I was dedicated I chose my path and I stuck to it. If one wants to get anywhere in life, one must set a course and sail stalwartly towards one destination; those who are at one moment tacking into the wind and the next flying before it, dissipate their energies and get nowhere. Tenacity achieves. Eternal questioning, self-doubt and misguided attempts to see issues from every point of view are the hallmarks of ineffectual liberalism.

Nowadays our young girls want to have their cake and eat it too. Not content with dismantling the customs and procedures which have taken many centuries to establish, they also try to combine normal family life with the nursing vocation. But it is as impossible now as it has always been. One can be a dutiful mother and wife, or one can be a Ward Sister; one still cannot do both.

Modern Sisters have lost their grip on tradition and their sense of duty; that is why they have lost their grip on the respect of those under them.

For my young correspondent, I have some simple advice. I recommend that she immediately resigns and undertakes at least another 15 years' staffing in a small provincial hospital such as St. Hilda's. You may find this difficult to believe, but even here, in this centre of clinical excellence, we are finding it increasingly difficult to attract the right kind of nurse, and there is a suitable vacancy on my ward at the moment.

If she should choose to spend a couple of decades with me, learning nursing the old way — with emphasis on discipline and 'swabbing the decks' — there will be no more talk of losing her grip.

How right her auxiliaries were to point out the sad decline in standards. We students were never allowed to speak to them unless it was to issue an order, and the Sister I trained with was proud to say that she never knew the surname of most of her auxiliary nurses, let alone their christian names. I am equally proud to continue that tradition.

The fact is, she is not ready for the challenges of her position. Yes, she may have completed a lengthy professional course, and numerous practical and written examinations; yes, she may have some management experience; yes, she may 'treat her patients as individuals'; yes, she probably knows all kinds of fancy things. Girls of her age usually do nowadays.

But to be a real Sister, one must be mature in years; one must call everybody by their surnames; and one must fold one's frilly impedimenta in an unusual and distinctive manner. This is the secret. Learn it well. The Welfare of our Patients is at Stake!

5 Special Occasions

Many critics have tried to define the magic of Angela Plume, but she is too rare a flower in the Garden of Letters to be pressed in any commonplace analytical canon.

On rare occasions, however, she allows us an insight into the motivations and personal chemistry which underpin her writings. The following 'occasional' pieces offer illuminating glimpses of the heart which beats beneath the navy blue uniform. Rejecting the limitations of the epistolary genre, Sister Plume is here seen in a variety of unwonted arenas, eloquent at the hustings, supportive to colleagues, and relaxed with the press.

Two of these articles first appeared in Christmas editions of the *Nursing Times*. Jollity and healthcare are no easy bedfellows, and Sister Plume is never frivolous. None the less, her sense of occasion is surely as great as any living writer's (though comparisons with Baudelaire are not without their appeal), and we may well savour her consummately skilful fusion of the mundane with the extraordinary.

Political Manifesto

A message to all voting members of the Royal College of Nursing

I am, and am proud to be, a good practical nurse. When I joined the Profession, many years ago, I knew my vocation was drawing me inveterately to the bedside of the sick and needy.

But I have had to stand by and watch the demise of this once great profession, as it has been pulled apart piece by piece. Pulled apart by educationalists and pseudointellectuals spouting quasi-marxism and perverting our young girls.

In the last few years the Royal College of Nursing has come to play a much more active and visible role in society; this is deeply regrettable. I have always considered — and espoused the view publicly — that the role of the nurse is to nurse. We should not tinker with medical autonomy, we should not embroil ourselves in party political in-fights and we should not be involved in educational philosophy.

Unfortunately, while those of us who nailed our colours to the adamantine principles of Florence Nightingale have been slaving away for the benefit of our patients, the seat of power within our own professional body has been violated. Violated, I say, by the very individuals who most threaten our society on other fronts. These radicals, with their beards and socialist views, are surely the least qualified to exert a wholesome influence on us as nurses.

I know, from the many messages of support I have received, that I speak for the vast silent majority of the nation's carers. This being the case, reluctant as I am to divert my energies from my responsibilities at the bedside, I feel the call to play a more influential role in the organisation of the RCN. I owe it to the countless numbers of ordinary work-a-day nurses.

I have bided my time, vigilant for the right opportunity to gain a foothold in the corridors of power. The time has come.

For the good of the Profession, and nurses everywhere, I offer myself for election to the Council of the Royal College of Nursing.

Like most nurses, I would normally be reluctant to put myself forward, and in taking to the hustings now, I do so with no thought of personal advancement.

Every crisis brings forth its leader, a figurehead behind which the forces of righteousness may muster. In all modesty, I can claim to be that figurehead.

My manifesto is simple, and familiar to all: I will spare no efforts in the fight for a return to the Victorian values which made this country, and our Profession, great.

I do not underestimate the challenge, or the strength of resistance we may expect from those who have promoted slackness and liberality for so many years. But with your support and an iron resolve, I am confident that we may finally be victorious.

Like any General leading a campaign I have my strategy, I have my tactics and I have my long-term objectives. The deeper complexities of political activity are probably beyond the grasp of my readers, and need not concern us here. I do, however, include a short list of the areas which I consider deserving of urgent action, if we are to reverse the downward trend of this once great Profession:

1. *Uniform* — An issue of paramount importance, which I know concerns us all within the Profession. I shall campaign tirelessly for the reintroduction of the State Badge. I shall petition for proper nurses' headgear, aprons and practical long skirts. I shall be relentless in my fight for lace cuffs.

In this quest I shall be fulfilling not just the wishes of the vast majority of nurses, but moreover those of the Medical Profession and the public at large who so deeply regret the loss of our traditional impedimenta. My clarion call shall be, 'Let nurses be recognised as a Profession once more, and allow us to wear our uniforms with pride.'

2.   *Political stance* — The RCN has always claimed to reject party political affiliations: fine words, but we have all seen the insidious march of left-wing policies into our hospitals. Nurses have been encouraged to take an interest in political matters that are not their concern. We have even seen undesirable elements within the College advocating the abolition of Rule 12, our one professional bulwark against Anarchy.

I shall reinstate true political impartiality. We must support those — of whatever political persuasion — who seek to strengthen the position of the family within society; those who encourage our people to be self-reliant rather than depending on a nanny state to coddle them; those who make society's soil fertile for the impregnation and nurturing of private enterprise; those who will oppose Bolshevism in all its forms.

3.   *Men* — I have written elsewhere of the damage that men have done to our Profession. I propose that the RCN should return to a strict policy of females only. Nursing is inherently and undeniably a female calling. Let people like Trevor Clay go and form their own organisation. Our message is clear: you're not wanted here!

4.   *Medical staff* — I shall seek to foster stronger links and working relationships with our colleagues, the doctors. As respect for Authority has declined, so doctors have had to face obliquity and impertinent questioning from patients and their so-called advocates. We as nurses must say that we are behind them in every respect, and proud to function under their guidance.

5.   *Advertising* — Like most nurses, I was outraged at the use of our funds to launch a propaganda campaign in the national press last year. This was clearly designed to undermine public confidence in our ability to cope. We all know that wards are

occasionally short staffed, but has it not ever been so? We learn our trade by *doing*, and a student nurse who finds herself in charge of a couple of wards on night duty should rejoice, and thank her lucky stars for such a valuable learning opportunity.

I shall campaign on your behalf against such advertising. We have never had any problem projecting an acceptable public image of the Profession in the past, so why spend millions of pounds promoting a subversive one? Remember colleagues, it was *your* money that was used!

6.   *Rank* — One of my new proposals will be for the formation of a new division within the RCN for nurses of the rank of Sister and above. It is clear that with the widespread and ill-advised abandonment of separate dining facilities and accommodation, respect for senior nurses has diminished.

I shall campaign for the reintroduction of such differentials. Further I advocate the distribution of a larger, more ornate ceremonial badge for senior nurses.

It is clear to me that those who have achieved a higher rank in the Profession, by virtue of their experience and dedication, should have more influence on the policies of the RCN.

With this in mind, I am in favour of introducing a weighted voting system. Students will of course continue to have no say in the College; qualified nurses will be granted one vote; Sisters and above will have five votes. Most members of the RCN are junior: the one nurse – one vote system has been responsible therefore for many of the wrong-headed decisions in the recent past. By evening up the voting power in favour of senior nurses, we may see RCN policy more closely reflecting the views of those who have contributed most to the Profession.

These then, are the foundation stones of my campaign. They are clearly the issues which nurses feel most strongly about, yet I am sure that I am the only candidate brave enough to address them head-on. Now, for the first time, your voice may be heard through mine. You may rest assured that I shall represent your interests fearlessly, untiringly and energetically.

Under the banner of 'Make Room For Plume', I am confident that we shall sweep to a glorious victory. Let us start to build a

Profession of which we may all be proud. Use your vote. The welfare of our patients is at stake!

Published on behalf of the MAKE ROOM FOR PLUME campaign, with assistance from the funds of Project 1860 (Trustee: A. Plume).

Interview

NT: Sister Plume, can I say how grateful we are to you for sparing us the time to talk to us about your life and times in nursing. Can I start by asking you what made you decide to become a nurse in the first place?

AP: I'd rather you began by sitting up straight, young man. Slouching is not only very bad for the posture, it is also a sign of a dissipated personality. When I was a girl, things were much better organised: what one did in life depended very much on who one's people were. My father travelled in supportive hose, and therefore was not in a position to make the connections necessary for an advantageous matrimonial alliance. However, a compassionate and caring nature, matched by a sturdy common sense, were universally remarked upon by those around me, and my mother took pains to secure me a place at one of the leading London hospitals at the earliest opportunity. Leaving my home in Dundee was something of a wrench, but I had found my vocation and family considerations were of secondary importance. My mother applauded my resolve.

NT: What was nursing like in the days when you first came into the profession?

AP: A far, far better thing in every respect. From the outset we were taught the importance of routine and discipline (and good posture!). There was much more domestic work.

Most of the early stages of my training were concerned with learning how to lay a fire, the importance of sprinkling water on the floor before sweeping the ward, and laundry practice. When the chores were complete, Sister would address the probationers on some aspect of care such as poulticing, or quiz us from Florence Nightingale's *Notes on Nursing*. I am still able to quote from this work, verbatim, and one cannot underestimate the benefit this ability has afforded me over the years.

NT: What do you miss most from that time?

AP: My uniform was much more elegant and professional then, even as a probationer, than any of the current fashions.

NT: What do you think of today's breed of nurse?

AP: If you mean those who have 'trained' in polytechnical colleges, then my opinions are well documented. They have been responsible for much of the deterioration in the status and professionalism of the nurse, and will do even more damage if unchallenged.

NT: You are of course one of the profession's most renowned and respected ward sisters. Have you ever been tempted to move into management or education?

AP: No, I have always seen my primary duty to lie with the alleviation of suffering at the bedside. I am of course both a manager and a teacher, exerting a positive influence on the patients and girls in my charge, but I fear my experience would be wasted in the bureaucratic slough which is modern health service administration. When the return to decent values comes, as I am sure it shall, I would consider any preferment that might be offered to me, but for the time being, I will not desert my patients.

NT: Has your new-won fame as a result of your widely read column in *NT* affected you in any way?

AP: No, of course not. In my own hospital I have long been accustomed to people seeking my advice on the important issues of hospital care. I am already famous in my hospital, and the column is intended merely to spread knowledge to a wider audience. I am, however, gratified by the numerous messages of support from my readers. I know that my column speaks for the majority of nurses who are all too often denied access to the media. I am merely the true voice of the nation's nurses.

NT: For the benefit of your large readership, could you give us a pen picture of yourself? What would you say were your strong points and — dare one say it — do you have any weak points?

AP: I don't know that people would be that interested. But suffice to say that the tribulations of a life's work have left surprisingly little mark on a robust, and some would say elegant, frame. But beauty is a transient thing, and I am pleased that it is my personality which those around me are most moved by. My virtues are those of any good practical nurse: self-discipline, a sense of duty and rigorous attention to detail. I am sure I have many weak points, although none spring to mind at the moment which seem worthy of comment.

NT: Could you give us some idea of what you do when you are not on the ward? Do you have any leisure activities of which you are particularly fond?

AP: I have been a leading member of the Darnall Methodist Rambling Club for many years, from which I derive great solace. I am also an avid collector of china mementoes from seaside towns, owning one or two items which I am assured are of great value and rarity.

NT: On a more personal level, has there ever been a Mr Right in your life — a doctor, perhaps — with whom you were on more than usually intimate terms?

AP: Young man, I am here to discuss a life's work in nursing, not to answer impertinent questions. Intimacy with doctors is an outrage, unless marriage is considered, and the demands of my vocation have made that impossible. Ask me something sensible.

NT: We are, of course, approaching the Christmas festivities. What changes to normal routine do you allow on your ward on Christmas day?

AP: As few as possible. Patients who are in a fragile state can be deeply disconcerted by changes in routine. My favourite analogy is that of bringing up children. Consistency is all. Behaviour that is unacceptable during the rest of the year is just as unacceptable at Christmas. I will of course extend the morning service to some 2 or 3 hours, and we look forward to the arrival of the Salvation Army band.

AP: Do you think visiting hours should be longer at Christmas?

NT: No. Relatives, especially children, tend to be even more insufferable at this time than any other, and I like to have the ward clear by 8 in the evening. However, I do allow visitors who have come a long way to stay for the full hour.

NT: What are your views about alcohol on the ward?

AP: White spirit is excellent for pressure sores, but it must be applied vigorously. I think it is generally agreed that egg white is just as effective.

NT: How do you ensure that Christmas disrupts the ward round as little as possible?

AP: Nothing disrupts the ward round. It is the crucial point of contact between the medical staff and myself, and takes place as usual.

NT: Should all but the most seriously ill be discharged at Christmas?

AP: All but the most seriously ill should be discharged at any time. I am not running a hotel. A patient is either ill, or he isn't. To avoid abuses of the system, I never discharge anybody in the week before or after Christmas.

NT: Will you be asking the consultant surgeon to cut the turkey? And how will you ensure that he cuts the right leg?

AP: I see somebody has been telling you about our little ritual! Yes well this *is* one of those little frivolities which we allow ourselves, dating back as it does for many years. Mr Flint is very accommodating, and last year surprised us all by arriving in fancy dress. We are still not sure what the purpose of his disguise was as he was caked from head to foot in soot, but he seemed in very good spirits. 'Be sure to leave some for my girls!' I told him, as he began. Fortunately the house officer was on hand to suture the minor flesh wound, which was caused by the knife being blunt and the table wobbling.

NT: Turning to more general issues of concern to the profession, do you have any advice about nurses' appearance? How could things be improved?

AP: As I have said, today's uniforms leave much to be desired, or rather they don't. One of the unique functions of the nurse is to maintain an appealing and graceful presence in the ward, for the edification of both patients and doctors. If I am given time, I can train a young girl to present herself well, hold her shoulders back and wash regularly; I can do nothing about a national uniform which seems to have been designed by a Cornish sailmaker on drugs. Where is the apron of yesteryear? Where is the rustle of starched linen? The glitter of a hard-won State Badge? The stately folds of a proper nurse's cap? If you want to improve things, you should bring back the traditional uniform, proven under battle conditions and a source of inspiration to patients of successive generations!

NT: Do you think nurses are properly rewarded?

AP: No, of course not. Nurses are paid far too much for the privilege of following their instinctive vocation. Students particularly should be petitioning for a cut in their training allowance, to prove once and for all that they have the interests of their patients at heart. At their age I would have lived on bread and water for the honour of being a nurse, and considered myself well-served even then! One expects nothing but whingeing from the trades unions, but in all honesty, what have they to complain about? I've always had enough for *my* wants, even though I *didn't* receive all that a devoted daughter might expect from her mother's posthumous financial arrangements.

My main fear is that with nurses' salaries spiralling ever upwards and out of control, we will attract **the wrong kind of person** into the profession. If we are not careful, by achieving the so-called 'living wage', we will lose our rightful place in the affections of the great British public. And you know how valuable the sympathy of the British public has been to us over the years!

NT: What should be the correct relationship between the doctor and nurse?

AP: It should be one of mutual respect. The nurse respects the doctor for his authority, his superior knowledge and his social status, whilst the doctor will respect the nurse because she carries out his instructions so ably and obediently.

The consultant fulfils the role of father, while the ward sister acts as a dutiful wife would in any family. Patients and nurses are the children to be cared for, nurtured and — where necessary — reprimanded. Junior doctors may be likened to visiting uncles, who are esteemed guests, subordinate only to the head of the family.

NT: Do you have any views on the use of computers on the ward? The Nursing Process and patient advocacy?

AP: Computers, to my mind, are the greatest confidence trick of the twentieth century. We all got on perfectly well without them, and they have brought no appreciable benefits since their arrival. I don't have any views about computers on the ward, because I would never allow them on my ward. I am told that one can play chequers against them. I have been playing chequers with the Reverend Fosdyke every Tuesday evening for 10 years. 2 hours a week of chequers is enough for anybody.

What was the other one? The Nursing Process? You are not an American are you, by any chance?

Patient advocacy is rather more interesting. I have often been in the position of acting as doctor's advocate, when the patient is too dim-witted or recalcitrant to understand that what is being done is being done for his own good. It is a vital part of any dutiful nurse's role.

NT: How do you react to the appointment of a woman, Edwina Currie, as junior health minister? Is she a good thing for nursing?

AP: Yes, what a fine ward sister she would have made! One only has to see how assured her manner is at the bedside during her numerous visits to our hospitals. Thank goodness the media are so frequently on hand to witness her genuine concern for the patients' suffering!

Of course, I was not surprised by the howls of outrage from the bolshevik elements in response to her common-sense analysis of the northern peoples. Truth will out, despite the raging of the mob!

If women are to go into politics, and it is not a development that has my unqualified approval, let them be the shining beacons of compassion exemplified by Mrs Currie. I have written to her, expressing my personal support for her stand, and I urge all my readers to do the same. (You may not have the ear of a nation as I do, but your letters will have their effect none the less.)

NT: What changes do you foresee in nursing by the year 2000?

AP: I see two futures, and which actually occurs will depend on my readers. First — and most bleakly — I see a nursing service laid low by the infiltration of American philosophies, men and liberalism; hospitals where the nurses don't wear hats and visitors come and go as they please; an end to the hierarchies and traditions which made our profession great, and an atmosphere of insecurity in which everything is open to question. You may well flinch young man: it **could** happen!

On the other hand if we, the silent majority, are resolute and outspoken, we may yet reinstate the principles of Florence Nightingale and establish a new Golden Age of British Nursing. It would be the crowning culmination to my life's work.

NT: Do you have a particular, seasonal message for your many thousands of readers?

AP: I would like to wish all my readers and friends a Happy Christmas and prosperous future. I trust they will not indulge in the excesses which are too often associated with this time of year. I hope they will join me in my crusade against the revolutionary elements in nursing, and call upon them to make their New Year's resolution a commitment to put their best foot forward, their shoulders to the wheel, and stand up and be counted. The welfare of our patients is at stake!

NT: Sister Plume, thank you, it has been a privilege.

AP: Yes, it probably has.

Memorabilia

To all Ward Sisters

Reference the Christmas period, can I draw the attention of all senior nurses to the recommendations of the Staff Consultative Committee, which were itemised in previous Staff Directive:SCC Memo 347b (Christmas)?

Last year the period of transition from functional to zonal management policy unhappily coincided with the Christmas period, the consequences of which I am sure we all remember too well. So much more important is it, then, that we should all pull together this year to minimise the disruption during the conversion back to functional management practice, especially as we will be in the middle of implementation mode at Christmas. Thank you in advance for your co-operation on this issue.

Merry Christmas.

G Statim

Geoffrey Statim
Unit Administrator

To Mr Statim
Office

If you would be so good as to furnish me with a copy of your latest memoranda translated into English I would be most grateful. Are you American by any chance? It seems to me that any chaos we have suffered has been caused by the interference of the so-called administration department in ward matters. I will have neither functional nor zonal management on my ward as we all have far too much to do already.

By the way, when will I receive my new desk diary? It seems to me that your department would be better employed if it concerned itself with the efficient supply of this urgently needed stationery. Leave the running of the wards to those who know what they are doing!

Merry Christmas.

Angela Plume

Sister A. Plume

To Sister Angela Plume

Dear Sister
It is our custom to erect a modest bran tub in the
children's ward at this festive time of the year, to
bring a little yuletide joy into the young ones' troubled
lives. Can you help in any way?

    Merry Christmas

J. Walker

    J. Walker
    Chaplain

To The Chaplain

Dear Vicar
I suggest you apply directly to the kitchen for your bran
supplies as I keep no more than three or four boxes on the ward.
Congratulations, however, on an innovative and nutritious way
of celebrating Christmas; far more sensible to my mind than
tinsel and silly paper hats.
    Have you received your 1989 desk diary yet?
    Season's greetings.

Angela Plume

    Sister Angela Plume

To The Matron

Dear Miss Linnet,
Can I confirm that the Nurses' Carol Service will be held
in the chapel as usual this year? I feel this is one
marvellous opportunity for all the nurses to worship
together. The vision of all our young girls -- in correct
uniform and singing a good old-fashioned marching carol --
is an inspiration. Last year's decision to allow the
girls to wear mufti was an unmitigated disaster, as
nobody could tell who was whom: there was at least one
student nurse sitting in the Sisters' pew!

I also think it would be a good idea to exclude the
patients from this event as they are apt to breach the
decorum of the service with requests for bedpans and the
like. Last year, a urology patient from Deidre Manners'
ward was seen using a urinal during a moving rendition of
As with Gladness Men of Old. I understand that this
was something of a watershed in that patient's treatment,
as he had been unable to pass urine for some hours prior.
None the less, this does not excuse his interruption of the
carol with the words, 'It's a miracle, there must be nigh
on three pints here'.

On another subject, we are experiencing significant
difficulties in obtaining our desk diaries for 1989. I
wonder if you have heard anything about them?

Merry Christmas.

Angela Plume

Sister Plume

To the Catering Services Manager

I confirm that Deidre Manners and I will be attending the
Sisters' Christmas Dinner on the 21st December. If the
other Ward Sisters in this hospital wish to fly in the
face of tradition and take their dinner with the ordinary
nurses on the 22nd December, that is up to them. Sister
Manners and I know our place, and our duty.
    I see no reason why we should not take our dinner in the
main refectory. I enclose a copy of the seating plan
indicating the table of preference. I trust that with
only two diners, there will at least be sufficient brandy
butter to go round, and a much higher standard of service
than we suffered last year.
    Please make a note of the date in your new desk diary,
which I understand you are fortunate enough to have
received already, through some administrative oversight.
    Merry Christmas.

Angela Plume (Sister)

From the Domestic Bursar
To Sister A. Plume

I am in receipt of a number of complaints from both the
public and hospital staff regarding a party which was
held in the nurses' home last night.

This unauthorised celebration involved the playing of
loud music far into the night, and junior members of
staff were seen dancing on the tennis lawns. Once again,
the recently refurbished bust of Mrs Millicent Throve
(Matron 1941-1953) has gone missing and foulplay is
suspected.

One of the nurses involved in this episode claims that
you gave your blessing and even encouragement to the
party. I find this difficult to believe. Can you shed
any light on the matter?

From Sister A. Plume
To the Domestic Bursar

I think there has indeed been some misunderstanding on
your part. The only event I have given my approval to
was last night's Vicars and Actresses Convention which
was to be held in the old dining room. As one of my
girls explained, this would provide an opportunity for
the church to confront, and hopefully redeem, those lost
souls who have abandoned themselves to the excesses of
the professional stage.

In fact I had the good fortune to meet one of the
clerical gentlemen in attendance last night, who is
indeed the twin brother of our very own Surgical
Registrar, Mr Johnson, and he confided to me that he was
very optimistic of making at least one conquest that
evening. I think we would all do well to throw our
support behind the Church Militant, and encourage their
endeavours.

I trust this clears up the misunderstanding. I suspect
that the complaints emanate from misanthropic troublemakers,
eager to resist the forces of righteousness.

A joyous Christmas to you. I understand you have already
received your 1989 desk diary. Why, I wonder, should a
non-patient department like yours receive stationery
supplies before the wards?

To Sister

Please may I request my two days off together at this
Xmas, as my parents live in Northumberland?

Many thanks.

Jane Mills

Student Nurse Mills

To SN Mills

I am afraid that there is absolutely no question of your
having two days off together over the Christmas period.
You may only be a student nurse, but I will still need
you on the ward as the public holidays offer excellent
opportunities for ward-cleaning: remember, Florence
Nightingale didn't see her family for years when she was
establishing this great Profession of ours, and she was
thousands of miles away in a foreign country that didn't
even celebrate Christmas!
   Moreover, there is much to be enjoyed in a ward
Christmas. There is the carol service of course, and we
shall be playing pin-the-tail-on-the-donkey as usual.
Mr Flint will carve the turkey again this year, and he
may even find time to have a few words with you. Most
importantly you will have the satisfaction of doing your
duty! How would it be if we all ran off to
Northumberland whenever the fancy took us?

Merry Christmas.

Angela Plume

Sister Plume

From Miss T. Linnet
To Sr. A. Plume

I note that you have some eight staff on every morning shift
over the Christmas period. Given the transport
difficulties over the public holidays, would it not be
viable to manage with fewer staff? This should be
possible if you are discharging your less-seriously ill
patients for Christmas.
    Merry Christmas.

        Miss T. Linnet

    T.L.

Dear Matron,
I always avoid discharging people home over the Christmas
period. I am not running a hotel for people who are ill
one moment and then breeze off home again when it suits
them. They are either ill or they are not.
    This being the case, I shall require a full complement of
staff to manage the ward. I am also keen to give my
younger girls a taste of a traditional ward Christmas.
They will do well to learn that their duty to the ward
comes before family considerations.
    You will appreciate that I was also forced to cancel
Christmas leave, because it was impossible to organise
the off-duty rota without the help of my new desk diary,
which I am still yet to receive. It may seem
a pity that my girls have to suffer because of the
administrative inefficiency of the other departments
within the hospital, but there it is.
    Why departments which have nothing to do with patient
care should receive their stationery before me is a
complete mystery. My resources are already stretched to
their limit; now I am reduced to compiling laundry lists
on bed-pan covers, and I may even have to purchase an
exercise book from Woolworths. Please let us confront
the stationery issue early in the new year. The welfare
of our patients is at stake!
    Merry Christmas,

        Angela Plume

    Sister A. Plume

Index

Academe, groves of 29
Accordion, piano 47
Age, Golden 37, 51, 90
Alcohol 60, 86
Almoner, Lady 7, 28, 46
Americans 26, 29, 35, 43, 46, 54, 55, 70, 89, 91
Australia, son in 6

Barton, Sue 36
        Bedpan washer, Armstrong Stroud Hydromatic 15, 34
Biscuits, Lincoln 69
Bottoms 1, 28
Bulwarks 30, 76

Capsules, glomerular 10
Communists 32, 66
Computers 89
Co-ordinator, Nursing Process 4
Crécy, battle of 51
Crimea, war of 22, 29, 41, 52
Chrysanthemums, plastic 15

Deaconesses, Order of 49
Doctors 2 *et seq.*, 58 *et seq.*, 81

Empire, Roman 31
Evacuation, nocturnal 12
Extensionism 39

Fleming 62
Forceps, Spencer–Wells 44
Friends, Society of 51

Games, Olympic 68
GNCC 28, 32, 35, 43, 53
Gin, pink 61
Giraffe, five-legged 22
Glassware, Gamages 11
Grease, elbow 73
Griffiths 20 *et seq.*
Guardsman, Grenadier 42

Harriet, Tom, Dick or 53
Herrings, red 49
Hilda's, Saint 76
Hispanic peoples 18
Hypocritus 49, 59, 62

Ideologies, half-baked 21
Illusionists, Italian 64
Institute, Universal Cleaning 73

Kildare, Doctor 62

Left wing, rabid 58
Lister 54
Liver Salts, Andrews' 54

Manners, Sister Deidre 75, 94
Marx 58

Nightingale, Florence 13, 25, 29, 34, 37, 44, 51–53, 71, 84, 90, 96
Nurses, male 2, 32, 38 *et seq.*, 50, 81

Oath, Hypocritical 49
Ombudsman, the 6

Pickfords 9
Plantain leaf, dried   61
Porridge, mess of   71
Project 1860   34, 37, 83
Project 2000   31–34, 36
Proportions, aberrant   14

RCN   28, 39, 43, 78 *et seq.*

St. John, Order of   50
Sandwiches   2
Sartre, John Paul   39
Shouldn't-be-seens   12
Simpson   54
Sisters, Augustan   50
Slough, bureaucratic   84
Society, share-owning   74
Standards, decline in   1 *et seq.*

State, nanny   81
Superiority, doctors'   88
Symposia, fatuous specialist   56

Throve, Millicent   95
Tidiness   13 *et seq.*

Uniform   42 *et seq.*, 84
Urine, goats'   63

Values, Victorian   37, 53, 80
Version, Authorised   47
View, woman's   23

Wellington, Duke of   52
WRVS   4
Wrong kind of person, the   88

Note: The author is indebted to Sister Deidre Manners for her valuable
assistance in the compilation of this important index.